**This book is to be returned on or before
the latest date stamped below.**

COTTON ARKWRIGHT

Cotton Arkwright

Master Spinner

A novel based on the life of
Sir Richard Arkwright

by

MARGARET ARKWRIGHT

ALTRINCHAM
JOHN SHERRATT AND SON LTD
and
E. J. MORTEN, PUBLISHERS
DIDSBURY, MANCHESTER

First published 1971
by E. J. Morten, Publishers,
4 Warburton Street, Didsbury, Manchester 20
and
John Sherratt and Son Ltd,
Park Road, Altrincham

SBN :
E. J. Morten: 901598 32 1
John Sherratt and Son Ltd: 85427 025 6

Made and printed in Great Britain
at the St. Ann's Press, Park Road, Altrincham

Contents

Chapter One

The Thirteenth Arkwright

"Proud Preston" had little reason to be proud of its weather on the night of December 23rd in the year 1732 for the rain was cascading down the window panes, and doors and windows shuddered with the impact of the strong winds which blew straight up the Ribble Estuary.

But, had the people known, the town did have some reason to be proud because one of its greatest sons, Richard Arkwright, was born that night, the man who became one of the founders of the Industrial Revolution which put this country in the forefront of the nations of the world in wealth and manufacture.

In the kitchen of a small working-class house in the town, there were ten young Arkwright children all quietly occupied in their own ways. The youngest was crawling along the floor and the next in age was toddling about and getting rather in the way of three more who were taking turns with a broom handle which did duty as a horse. Three more were busy peeling potatoes at the slop stone and two sat spinning at their wheels as close to the fire as they could get. Two older children were still out doing the odd jobs which brought in the extra coppers to augment the meagre wages of their father, and the thirteenth child was now struggling his way into the hard world of the poor in a room upstairs.

There was little room for furniture in this over-populated kitchen. Bonnets and shawls hung on pegs on the wall and beneath them, arranged in order of

7

size, was a neat row of clogs. A large iron basket containing loaves of bread was suspended from the rafters and at one side of the fire was an oven in which the bread was baked twice a week. The girdle stone on the fire was used to bake flat oat cakes. Apart from a number of stools the main item of furniture was a well-scrubbed deal table now covered with a spotlessly clean cloth for the evening meal.

Thomas Arkwright hurried in from his day's work, hung up his worn jacket on a vacant peg, kicked off his clogs, placed them neatly at the head of the row and went straight upstairs. He was really dismayed at the thought of "one more for the porridge bowl" and, as he climbed the stairs, he found himself hoping that his thirteenth child would not survive its birth—unworthy thought, but it was hard enough to remain respectable on his wage and the coppers of his eldest children, and the arrival of yet another mouth to feed made his heart sink.

The midwife stumped downstairs for a kettle of boiling water and the children suddenly became quiet as she entered the kitchen—Mrs. Clough was a necessary but not popular visitor to the house and the children were afraid of her.

Then the front door was opened again bringing the rain blowing onto the kitchen floor and the two eldest came in, red-cheeked and with freezing cold hands.

"How long afore us can eat?" one of them asked as they both rushed to the fire, holding out their hands to the warmth and squatting on the heels of their clogs. "We're fair clemmed."

An enormous cauldron of potatoes had just been placed on the stove and there were jugs of milk on the table. This was their staple diet, but it filled the great gaps in their stomachs, which were permanently aching with hunger.

"The boss be giving me some black puddens tomorrow," said the eldest boy. "He said they were to be my Christmas box—but that's not today," he added sadly.

"Has Father come in?" queried the other. He was not so much curious as anxious about their meal, for which their mother always made them wait until the head of the family should be there.

"You know what's to do," said Dorothy looking up from her spinning. "The midwife's been here more'n half an hour."

Nobody showed the slightest interest; all it meant was a filling of the old cradle, only just vacated, and more heavy jobs like scrubbing, to do for their mother.

"When can us eat?" demanded John the eldest boy leaning forward to prod the potatoes with a long fork, then hurriedly replacing it as their father's footsteps were heard descending the stairs.

"You'm all got another brother," said Thomas Arkwright heavily, and he strode to the slop stone to wash his hands. "Gimme a loaf," he added tersely, "and I'll take a bowl of bread and milk to thy mother."

Dorothy quickly filled a shallow pan with milk to be warmed, and Thomas, with big, competent hands, cut the bread into small squares. "I reckon she could do with a bit of sugar," he continued in a depressed voice. Then as he watched the milk warming, he put his hand in his pocket and produced a small bottle of gin.

"Now that's nobbut for Mrs. Clough," he said, firmly placing it in the middle of the table. "And don't any of you touch yon. And when Mrs. Clough has had her drop we can eat our suppers; the little ones can have a taste of milk now, but nobbut else. We don't want her to catch us eating."

There was a general sigh of agreement. It would be

little short of tragic if Mrs. Clough were to sit down with them when there was barely enough to go round.

Thomas poured the warm milk onto his carefully-cut bread and disappeared upstairs again. As the bedroom door opened for a moment, a thin, high wail was heard coming from above.

"Off we go!" said John the eldest, and as if in a sign of vigorous companionship, the two youngest raised their voices and howled also. "There's another one come to cry with thee," said their brother, then he leaned forward, seized the two babies and placing one on each knee, proceeded to jog them up and down. He was a kind lad and though he had reached the age when he was glad to get out of the packed house and into the streets nearby, he was fond of his myriad brothers and sisters.

It was better in summer time, but in winter when the days were long and dark and often wet, one could hardly move for children in the small, clean kitchen.

Thomas could never afford any education for them and there were no schools in Preston, except paying dame-schools which were beyond his means, so that there was little to occupy the small ones until they reached the age of being taught to spin.

Some of them were fretting noisily as Mrs. Clough descended the stairs with a bucket and went out to the square where everyone threw their rubbish into the stream which flowed through. She came in hanging the damp shawl she had been wearing onto the back of a chair, and sat down heavily, her eyes travelling quickly to the bottle of gin on the table.

"Your Ma's awreet," she announced, though nobody enquired. "But it were a rough job."

Thomas closed the bedroom door and come down to join her.

He opened the bottle, poured some hot water and gin into two cups, and said shortly, "I'm very much obliged to you, Mrs. Clough."

Mrs. Clough held out her hand. "Same as usual," she commented briefly and a coin passed between them; Thomas refilled her cup, the contents of which had disappeared in one.

"Well, let's hope it's the last time," he said, and after what seemed to the waiting children a protracted silence, Mrs. Clough drained her cup, put on her shawl and disappeared into the dark night.

"Now we can eat!" exclaimed Thomas. "And I've got summat to tell thee all. Pigs' trotters tomorrow! And a joint of pork for Christmas, for I'm going to kill our pig in the morning!"

There was a sigh of pure delight.

"A mooney Christmas!" cried John, for a pig had to be killed at the waxing of the moon. Pigs' trotters and black puddings, not to mention a leg of pork, was undreamed-of feasting, for Christmas to the Arkwright family was simply thought of in terms of food, and no doubt Uncle Richard would bring them something for Christmas Day itself. He was a prosperous uncle with no children of his own and at Christmas he never forgot the hungry mouths in Thomas's house.

The potatoes and milk being finished, the dishes were washed up, the table-cloth folded, and the two youngest popped side by side into a bed which stood in a corner of the kitchen. Two more would presently join them, sleeping at the other end, and the remaining ones were secretly jealous as they climbed the stairs to the cold rooms which they all shared.

It was a hard and wearing life for the whole family, with no time left over for enjoyment of any kind. The two elder girls who were scarcely more than children, were hired as domestic helps at one of the bigger houses in Preston, but came home to sleep; the boys got what jobs they could round about, whilst Thomas was a smallholder on the outskirts of the town, scraping a sparse living, and filling every off moment by doing his turn at the spinning wheel.

His brother Richard Arkwright was distinctly more prosperous. With nobody to look after but himself and being of a thrifty, careful nature where every penny was saved and watched over, he still did what he could for the struggling family who were his only relatives. He was respectable, steady and a regular church-goer and where Thomas had to do any and every sort of job to support his ever-growing mob of children, Richard had been able to devote hours to night-school, and could not only read and write, but knew his figures.

He came round to supper the night after the new baby was born, bringing with him the eagerly awaited parcel containing a large plum pudding tied up in a cloth and a meat pie as well, and his nephews and nieces crowded round him.

"I've heard the news," he remarked to Thomas as he sank into the best chair and the little ones crawled over him. "A boy, they tell me? Well, and how many does that make?"

"Thirteen," said Thomas glumly. "And we could have done without him, but there, 'tis God's will."

"And I think thee had summut to do with it!" chuckled Richard. "'Tis hard for the Missis, nobbut you'll both be glad of children when you grows older. I came to ask if thee was awreet for brass over Christmas because I've got a bit to spare and thee's reet welcome to it."

Thomas laid a hand on his brother's arm.

"I wouldna say no!" he answered briefly. "We're

always on the short side and this baby coming hasn't made things no easier; but they're all good young 'uns and we'll get by in the end. I was going to ask if thee'd be godfather to this boy what has come along? We'd thought of calling him Richard too, if thee had a mind to it?"

Uncle Richard thought hard then said slowly after a long pause : "Well, I don't mind if thee does! It might be summut for me to keep an eye on a young lad! But I don't want him yet awhile!" he finished quickly.

"Thee's a good man," said Thomas gratefully. "Come and draw up to the table and have a bite o' summut with us, and then I'll take thee to see thy godson. Thirteen!" he added ruminating. "Lucky for some! And perhaps young Richard's going to be the lucky one!"

They christened young Richard at the Parish church on New Year's Eve; his uncle was present and those of his brothers and sisters who could be spared from their jobs. His mother looked frail and found it a dragging walk but she was buoyed up with the thought of Uncle Richard's promises over the little lad and found comfort in the fact that the tiny creature lay without crying in his godfather's arms and never even opened his eyes.

Perhaps Thomas was right and thirteen was going to prove a lucky number.

Richard grew up a strong and lusty boy, except for a tendency to occasional attacks of asthma, and as soon as he was able to trot along the streets of Preston, he went to live with his uncle and relieved the congestion at home.

Although he could well afford to send young Richard to a dame-school, partly through thrift and partly because he was genuinely fond of and interested in the little boy, the older Richard taught him to read on his own.

13

It was a hard struggle; young Richard was as bright as a button, but utterly refused to concentrate. His Uncle never knew afterwards how he had the patience to continue teaching the wriggling little creature who was entranced with anybody or anything passing the window whilst he was doing his lessons and had only one passionate longing—to finish his work and dash into the streets where he had innumerable friends.

Writing was a desperately hard task, but second to the dreadful difficulty of learning to read, and it was only figures that came at all easily.

"He seems bright enough except at his books," said Uncle Richard rather sourly to Thomas. "But I shan't give up! There's something to the lad, and one day he'll live to regret his dumbness." Which was indeed true.

The most valuable gift which Richard the elder passed on to his young pupil, was thrift and economy; not one penny was ever wasted or spent without the most careful thought, and young Richard grew up never to squander.

He was a cheerful, good-natured boy, racing round with his friends who congregated waiting for him outside his Uncle's house, but spend one half-penny piece he would not and, when the first coin was dropped into his hand as a tip, he put it safely away. His store of savings only grew with extreme slowness, depending on his chances of finding errands to be run or horses to be held whilst their owners went into the inn for a pint of ale. Every penny he could muster was stored in a tin box under his bed and, as the small sums increased, so Richard gloated.

His uncle had drummed into him that no poor man would ever be really respected, and when Richard's friends spent their money on lollipops and fairings, he would fade into the background and walk away. He was very popular in spite of these careful habits and it was quite a grief to the gangs of boys who played in the streets, when Uncle Richard announced that he was to go to night-school and give up these frivolous evenings.

Richard was thunderstruck at this fearsome order; he failed to see why he was not allowed to live the life his brothers and sisters lived, for they helped on the little farm, did odd jobs and took their turns at the spinning wheels all in their own time and it was a life of freedom as long as the work was done.

Night-school was a period of complete drudgery, for all forms of education were anathema to him but his uncle was adamant and must have had some strange foresight of the lad's intelligence for he never relaxed from his strict upbringing, his stress on the value of care and saving, and the ultimate good that schooling would do. He had great ambitions for his nephew and wondered if there might be an opening in the cotton trade but found himself full of doubts because of Richard's lack of brains over his books.

It was a day of tremendous disappointment to him when Richard came home and announced that he wished to become apprenticed to the local barber who had said he was ready to take him on as a "lather boy", and Uncle Richard felt that all the trouble he had taken in attempting his nephew's education had been brought to nothing.

"I want to start earning some brass," said Richard firmly, "and he can tek me on straight away."

"Seems as if there should be better openings than that," grumbled his Uncle. "I shouldn't be surprised if there wasn't something in the cotton trade with all this demand for spun yarn. Why have all yon chaps come over from Flanders to Manchester and Rochdale if there isn't something doing? I should have thought you might try for a job in that line where there's a bit of prospect. Where's barbering going to lead you?"

"You can't do anything without brass," said Richard doggedly. "And this is as good a chance as any in Preston. Anyway I'll try it for a week or two and give up my night-school."

"You'll regret that," said his Uncle. "The day'll come when you'll thank me for teaching you summut; times are changing, and its book-learning as will get you on in t'world."

But young Richard was tiresomely stubborn and the next morning raced off to start his apprenticeship with a barber named Nicholson.

He enjoyed his work and was thankful to get away from the studies which were all too tame for a vigorous boy and appeared to have no bearing on his future life. At any rate from an early age, he became financially independent.

Chapter Two

The Subterranean Barber

Nicholson was a hard task-master; his lather boy was kept at it from early morning until late at night and never for a moment allowed to relax or become slip-shod in his work.

Richard was very strictly trained and, to the great surprise of his Uncle, remained stolidly working at his job for over three years. He was paid little but he had his tips and part of what he earned was meticulously saved so that the amount grew year by year.

There was no more larking about with the young lads of Preston; the longer hours he worked, the more he was able to put by, and though useless at book-learning, Richard was brainy enough to seize every opportunity of gaining practical knowledge and, during his years of apprenticeship, he cultivated a keen sense of observation and found his brain was teeming with ideas.

This was the era of wigs and perukes and part of his job was to wash them and comb them and retint the portions where the dye had either been rained on or burnt by the sun, leaving the wig in a sorry state.

"There should be a dye what doesn't fade," said Richard to Mr. Nicholson. "It's being used in textiles and I don't see why it can't be used on hair."

Nicholson grunted and thought it a far-fetched idea.

"Stop thinking nonsense and get on with the job!" he said shortly.

But Richard was convinced that there was no non-

17

sense at all in his thinking and, with his inborn dogged-
ness and faith in himself, he obtained some dye from
friends in the textile industry and conducted his experiments in his uncle's kitchen. He succeeded in making a
great mess as well as infuriating his uncle, but he failed
to make the hair take on any lasting colour to withstand
sun and rain.

Under the instruction of Nicholson he soon learned
the art of wig-making and, with his youth and likeable
personality he was much more successful in getting the
local girls to sell pieces of their hair, than was his master.
He soon became a valuable assistant in the business and,
with his firm belief that money was essential to success,
he went on saving as much of his wages as he possibly
could.

Although Uncle Richard lived comfortably and saw
that young Richard had a good home, he lived thriftily,
so that when he died he was able to leave a small legacy
to his nephew. This capital sum, though little enough,
when added to his savings was a turning point in the
life of Richard Arkwright. He felt he was already on
the road to becoming a millionaire. With money in his
purse but no home to live in, he decided to leave Preston
and seek his fortune in Bolton where cotton manufacture
was beginning to boom. Sending his few belongings by
coach he decided to walk the fifteen miles or so by the
shortest route over the moors.

After walking for about two hours across the plain
through Walton-le-Dale and Hoghton he began the long
climb to Belmont passing between Hollinshead Hall and
Withnell Moor.

Contrary to common belief, it is not always raining in
Lancashire and up on the moors the air was pure and
fresh as he swung along the rough track. He had always
been subject to attacks of asthma when working in the

shop but here on the moors with a wide expanse of sky
and far-ranging views across the plain towards the sands
of Southport he really felt on top of the world. His heart
was full of optimism for the future and his high position
on the hills seemed to foreshadow an equally high position in industry and future wealth. He chose to stop for
a brief spell at a point near Belmont where the view was
grandest. In a hollow sheltered from the wind and enjoying to the full the warmth of the sun, he ate his hunk of
bread and potted pilchards with a draught of home-
brewed ale, enthralled by the sound of larks singing high
in the sky and the occasional raucous cry of a cock
grouse. Life was good, and Richard felt that the wind of
change was gusting within him. Gathering up the leather
bag which contained all his worldly wealth in good
money he set off down the valley where he soon began
to meet people who greeted him kindly in the way that
country folk have. There was something about his neat
appearance, his upright and confident attitude and his
friendly, honest look that appealed even to the gentlemen
on horseback whom he encountered and who stopped
and chatted to him.

"A fine morning!" one of them called cheerfully.
"Where are you off to, my lad? You look in pretty good
spirits!"

"Aye, I am an' all!" answered Richard, impressed by
the cultured voice which he was hearing for the first time
in his life. "I'm a barber by trade, sir, and am hoping to
find a job in Bolton."

"You'll find plenty of pretty girls at any rate, all busy
with their spinning wheels," said the unknown gentleman. "You'll be marrying one of them afore you can
turn around."

"Not me, sir!" answered Richard perkily. "I've got
to find a good job first, and prove that I know how to

make a wig—and dye it, sir, so that it don't run in the rain!"

"You'll make a fortune if you can do that!" laughed the unknown horseman, who must have looked back later in life to this day of prophecy. "Go to my friend Edward Pollitt, the peruke maker, and ask him from me, to give you a job!" He spurred his horse and rode off without even telling Richard his name, but looking after him as he galloped over the moor, Richard memorised his features, and made up his mind to go straight to Edward Pollitt and tell him of the gentleman who had instructed him to apply for work.

On the road near Astley Bridge he was overtaken by a carter on his way to Bolton who willingly gave the tired youth a lift into the town and recommended a cheap and clean lodging where, after a hearty meal, he dropped on to his bed and slept soundly through the night.

Mr. Pollitt was very favourably impressed by the young man who came to him next morning—from his answers to searching questions, obviously well skilled in the art of wig making. But to make wigs one must have hair and Mr. Pollitt guessed what Nicholson had proved—that this young man was capable of charming the hair from the heads of the local girls far more successfully than he could. Deciding forthwith to employ Richard he sent him at once round the local fairs with this special mission. Girls who were available for domestic service would stand in the centre of the market place, spruce in their clean white aprons, offering themselves for hire, and when Richard came along and admired their hair, they would giggle at first and then let themselves be persuaded to part with a few locks.

"Your curls are worth a lot to me," Richard said to one girl with charming golden tresses. "Why don't you make a shilling or two now, and in no time you hair will grow again, and you won't remember you ever lost it!"

At long last one girl consented, and Richard, knowing his trade, cut her hair so well that she looked just as attractive when it was short.

Encouraged, several other girls joined in, happy to have some money in their pockets while they were waiting to be hired and anyway what difference did it make to their appearance when their locks were always tucked inside their mob caps?

Mr. Pollitt was delighted. He hired a horse for Richard, who could then get further afield, and as well as visiting the fairs he called at houses where girls were spinning at home and each time came back to the shop laden with his spoils.

This was a life which he really enjoyed; he was an indefatigable worker and when he returned from a long day's outing, he sat down straight away to his wig-making or turned his hand to shaving. The good training with Nicholson proved its worth; not only did he make smart wigs and shave the customers with ability, but he was gentle and firm at blood-letting and tooth-drawing and the gentlemen of the town began to ask for him personally.

"Where's the boy?" they would say to Pollitt as they entered his shop, although Richard was now eighteen years old. "Gone off to the fairs again? Well, I'll wait until he can see to my tooth for me," and the gentlemen would walk out.

Pollitt realised he had made a good bargain in employing Richard; he himself was getting older now but his business, instead of going downhill, was rapidly on the up-grade and he did not hesitate to raise Richard's wages.

Richard's thrift continued with the years. His store of savings was now quite large; he was sober and hard-working, but his head was full of dreams of a wonderful

21

future. It never struck him that he could be anything but an enormous success and one day he was determined to find the answer to the fast dyes for which he was seeking.

It was a big chance for him when Pollitt died, peacefully and happily, feeling sure that his widow would be well looked after by Richard, and that he need feel no fears for his business.

"I shan't leave thee," promised Richard to Mrs. Pollitt after her husband's funeral and he saw to it that in spite of the death of the owner, the shop should only be closed for half a day whilst he went with the weeping wife to pay his last respects.

The clientele of the shop had rapidly improved since his arrival and Richard went out of his way to give satisfaction to his superior and better dressed customers. He always liked people of a higher social standing than himself and they in turn began to rely on him more and more, not only for hairdressing and shaving but for the minor physical operations which he did so efficiently.

He had now been in Bolton for three years, was well known in the town and extremely well liked. He was always so neat in appearance and so decently dressed that people gave him credit for being of a higher class than he really was.

It was at church that he became acquainted with Robert Holt, a schoolmaster, and it was not long before he was invited to Mr. Holt's extremely respectable house and to meet his attractive daughter, Patience.

Patience was a pretty, fair girl with a charming, deprecatory manner, yet with a quiet dignity. She ran the house for her father, was well-trained in domestic duties and of good education.

Richard admired her very much for knowing all the sort of things which he did not, and for the first but not the last time in his life, was conscious of his lack of learning though his genial character, his hard-working ways and his general charm made up for his shortcomings.

It became an understood thing that after Morning Service, he should return with Robert Holt and his daughter for dinner in the afternoon. It was the only day of the week on which he did not work and sometimes he was permitted to take Patience for a short walk during which he used to confide to her his dreams and aspirations.

"There's a fortune to be made if only I could get hold on the way to make a fast dye," he would say, as some fanciful dandy strolled by in a plaited peruke, perhaps with a silk knot at the nape of the neck. "You see yon gentleman—if he gets caught in the rain, the colour of his brown wig will come pouring down that satin coat of his and not only will he have to get a new coat, but his wig done up as well and that'll cost him anything from one to three guineas!"

Patience listened admiringly for she, too, was utterly convinced of Richard's eventual success. She found that she was very much in love with him and hoped he would ask her to marry him but Richard, desperately in love himself, was terrified that his financial position did not warrant a proposal of marriage.

Having stuck to his bargain to see Pollitt's widow no longer in any danger of want, he decided he would strike out and take a shop which he could really call his own. All he could afford was a place in a dark cellar with steep steps leading down to the depths and only the red and white pole outside to tell customers where he could be found.

It was disheartening at first to stand waiting below and hear men stop at the entrance and then, faced by the gloomy stairs, walk away muttering.

His old clients at Pollitt's prophesied that he would

not prosper in business in the cellar and it certainly seemed to Richard that they could well be correct, but all was not lost. His skill and patience with the clients at the old shop was such that they were very loth to leave him even though he practised in a cellar. There was one gentleman who insisted on coming and who stood at street level and shouted down to Richard to come up and help him down to the shop.

Patience suggested that he put up a sign in the street *The Subterranean Barber—A clean shave for* 1d which delighted Richard so much that the sign was up in no time and the tide began to turn. Gentlemen passing by not only nudged each other and remarked on the sign but some decided to give this subterranean barber a trial. They could always go elsewhere if they were not satisfied, but when they found how carefully and efficiently they were shaved they not only came regularly but spread the news about the town so that very soon Richard's shop became the most popular and fashionable in Bolton.

In order to get their clients to return, the other barbers in the town also reduced their charges to one penny and Richard lost some of his trade in consequence. Not to be defeated, he decided to offer a clean shave for one halfpenny and at street level he flaunted a new notice:

> *Halt! Stop! What do you think?*
> *Shave for a ha'penny and give you a drink?*

but when the customers descended the steps to the shop, they were confronted with another notice:

> *Halt! Stop! What? Do you think*
> *That I'd shave for a ha'penny* and *give you a drink?*

Customers were by then in the shop and stayed for a

shave—amused at the trick but very satisfied with the quality and cheapness of the service.

Richard Arkwright was a man who could not accept defeat in any project to which he had set his mind and heart, and the discovery of a fast dye for hair had been eluding him since the early days when he experimented in his uncle's kitchen in Preston. Now, in the kitchen at the back of his shop, he was working by day and often far into the night on the problem and always hoping for a solution as his knowledge increased and his methods improved. He carefully recorded each experiment so that when the discovery was made and the colour of the hair remained fast and proof against the water and sunlight, he would know exactly how the process had been made.

There came a day when, almost to his disbelief, he examined the hairs after being soaked and exposed to the sun, and the colour was still there—the cloth on which they lay was as clean and white as when he placed them on it! He could not believe that he had succeeded and repeated the process with, if anything, more of a soaking and with longer exposure; he could hardly bear the strain when he returned to the hair to check, but there it was, fast dyed as before.

As soon as he could he rushed off to the house of the schoolmaster with the news of his success. Patience belied her name on this great occasion and insisted upon returning with him to see the magnificent locks of bright chestnut hair steeped in cold water and without a hint of dye staining the water. The two young people just stood gaping at the sight, hand in hand, in happy silence until the spell broke. They looked at each other for a second, and then both burst into laughter to ease the tension of the moment.

Richard lost no time in cashing in on his discovery. He

had cards printed by Walter Barlow which were distributed throughout the town and district.

Richard Arkwright
Peruke Maker,
In Bolton
Hair cut etc, in the neatest and best fashion
Maker of all sorts of Perukes, Ladies' Tates
and locks
May be had also several sorts of cut,
curl, scratch and dyes.
Bob Perukes at reasonable prices.

Once more the shop became full of clients. His perukes were famous and gentlemen from all around sent for them. Richard Arkwright himself certainly had his hands full and worked all hours to satisfy the new demands but he was a tireless worker, especially when the rewards were so great. He guarded his secret from his fellow barbers in the town who would have gone to any length to obtain it. This meant that he alone, mixed his dyes and applied them for he would not trust anybody even to assist him in the process. He could no longer travel about to buy hair and for this he engaged a travelling assistant.

As if this was not enough Richard Arkwright started a business in patent medicines and advertised "The right Daff's Elixir and Godfrey's Cordial" about town, and, as a moderately rich man, he judged the time to be ripe to approach the schoolmaster for the hand of his daughter Patience. Mr. Holt willingly gave his consent and Richard Arkwright married Patience Holt to their mutual joy. There was, in any case, no question of Patience marrying beneath her, for barbers of the highest class were highly thought of, especially as the best men were skilled in many of the arts of the surgeon and had,

The Old Market Place, Deansgate, Bolton

therefore, almost the same standing as doctors in the community.

Richard installed his wife in a house in Deansgate—a very respectable neighbourhood in Bolton—where she fulfilled her housewifely duties proudly and efficiently for her hard-working but very successful husband.

These days with Patience in their own house were days of great happiness for them both. It is probably true to say that this period had a joy which was never equalled and never repeated during the whole of his life that followed. He became a great industrialist, extremely wealthy and a man honoured by his king but the bliss of his early married life with Patience remained in his memory to his death.

Richard and Patience were deeply in love and although they were brought up in different traditions, there was a strong bond which bound them together and gave them both great joy.

Patience had the education and polish which he lacked. Richard was immensely proud of his excellent wife and took every opportunity in his busy life to entertain his friends in good style. Patience was a splendid cook and housewife. She cooked and baked, brewed ale, made pikelets which were justly famous and was renowned for her jellies and pickles. But more than this she was a woman of sweetness and gentle manners.

Richard, on the other hand, could be uproarious with his friends when he relaxed at home. His speech often relapsed into the broadest Lancastrian dialect, but, all the time, he was a man of integrity and sound north country commonsense and respected accordingly by all.

Chapter Three

A Great Loss

A barber hears a lot from his clients—some local scandal, local news, comments on national news and much about the state of industry and farming, local and national. This gossip and exchange of views was far more interesting and valuable in the eighteenth century when there was no radio and television and when newspapers were scarce or unobtainable.

"There's so much discontent in Lancashire," he said to Patience one night, "that I cannot believe in the joy of coming back to you every evening. There's agitation going on with the spinners and so much talk of how the work can be done by machines, that there's little else spoken of in Bolton these days. They are all talking in the shop about the effect these machines will have on employment and there is real fear amongst the spinners that their jobs will be taken from them."

"I don't see how anything could," said Patience, to whom the working of the cotton industry was a closed book.

"You see, love, you've never had to do it," explained Richard. "But people spinning in their own homes—some of them children as my brothers and sisters were—spin stuff they call yarn, and that's what the weavers want for making materials. Three spinners can hardly keep one weaver going and you'll see men walking from town to town, trying to collect the yarn they need, and now they say that chaps are working all ends up to invent machines which will keep up with the demand."

"Anyway it's got nothing to do with barbering," said Patience simply.

"It's got nought to do with it," said Richard. "But the chap that discovers how to work more spindles at a time and quickly, has got a fortune coming to him."

"I don't suppose the spinsters would think much of him," said Patience at once. "Where would their bread and butter come from I'd like to know?"

"There'd be so much cotton material wanted and made, the whole lot of 'em would get employment!" said Richard. "I'd like to be the one that found out how it could be done, and I don't see that it'd be all *that* difficult once you've got started. There was a lad in the shop only this morning saying as how the Chinese have got some such machine and I want to get hold of him again to tell me what he knows."

"You always were a man for anything new!" said Patience, lovingly. "But you be content with your hair dye, love, though I know you're a rare one for wheels and such like, for look what you did to our clock!"

Perpetual motion had a great fascination for Richard, as had anything mechanical, and in his cellar he had a clock with all the appearance of being worked by smoke from the chimney, to the mystification of many of his customers.

Although it was purely an outside interest, Richard could not help being stirred by the conversations he heard going on around him and he longed to find out what was afoot.

There was a feverish atmosphere in Lancashire, as if the country were on the brink of some great discovery, but nobody seemed successful, although there were rumours of men working in cellars and garrets to overcome the heartbreaking shortage of yarn. Weavers walked from town to town desperately searching, whilst looms stood idle, and Richard also knew of the under-current of interest in a trade which lagged far behind the wool industry.

Dark gentlemen from Cyprus and Turkey often came to his barber's shop, intent on selling raw cotton, and the need for a fabric which could stand up to `frequent washing was only too apparent. Woollen clothing could certainly be an offence, for it was unable to bear many visits to the wash-tub and even elegant ladies of fashion found a back-scratcher was a necessity of life.

But Richard had little time to fiddle about with wheels and wires, though he listened fascinated whilst men talked, and occasionally amused himself of an evening at home by playing with bits of machinery.

Otherwise life was too smooth-running and too happy to be disturbed by outside events; he saved money, and Patience was just as careful and thrifty as he was himself, so there was never a discordant note and to visit his house was to see a scene of domestic bliss unmarred by any disputes or worries.

The arrival of a small son was the crowning event in their happy lives, and though it seemed to take time for Patience to recover from the event, they took little notice of it and were as rapturously proud of young Dick as young parents invariably are, and quite unperturbed that his mother had lost some of her attractive youthfulness in bringing him into the world.

"I have everything that I could possibly want," Patience confided to Richard as they took an afternoon stroll one Sunday together. "Could any woman be more blessed? If only I could feel a little stronger!"

That was the one thing that worried Richard; Patience had never seemed so energetic or looked quite as healthy since Dick had arrived but she did not let it be of great account. The house was just as impeccably managed, the good Lancashire dishes just as plentiful— the black puddings, the pigs' trotters, the oatcakes, the tasty hot-pots, which in Richard's young days had been only of potatoes and onions, but were now filled with steak and kidney.

Once or twice when Richard returned home late after an unusually large order for dyed hair he found Patience, who always waited for him at whatever hour he came home, had gone to bed early and was in an exhausted and deep sleep. Little Dick welcomed him with a shout from his cot but Patience slept dreamlessly on undisturbed.

"You did not hear me come to bed?" said Richard a little anxiously the following morning.

"I was so tired, love," said Patience. "I don't know why, but I did a big bake, and then it was such a fine day, perhaps I walked a bit further than usual with Dick and got tired pushing his chair up the brew. Did you get your supper which I left in the oven?"

"Aye, and I was reet clemmed," said Richard in his broadest Lancashire dialect which he used when he was in a joking mood. Patience had a more refined voice, rather like some of his distinguished customers, and Richard tried to improve his own way of speaking, but it never ceased to be something of an effort and he was glad to slip back into the real dialect when he bargained for hair or talked to his apprentices.

"I shouldna' do so much today," he went on, putting his arms around her as they lay in bed. "Thee must not overtire thyself."

Patience slipped out of his embrace and got hurriedly to her feet.

"It's nothing!" she said crossly. "What a fuss you do make, Richard! Can't a girl feel a bit tired now and again? Beside I had finished the book Father gave me to read and it was dull sitting by the fire alone."

"It's funny that," said Richard, getting out of bed. "You know reading don't come easy to me but there's nothing I like better than sitting down and just thinking or fiddling about with odd jobs. Now I reet enjoyed that evening when the clock stopped and I got it going again!"

It was quite true; he had a very handy way with anything mechanical and, though mathematics had been the easiest of the subject he had attempted in his youth, he had never advanced very far in their study. Now he would spend hours "cutting pasteboard into different shapes, such as forming squares from oblongs without adding or diminishing, and a hundred knacky thinks one cannot find words to explain," as Dick was to learn many years later when he was finding out about his father's early married life.

His big sturdy fingers loved playing about with small neat objects and he would become absorbed and silent, which never bothered Patience because she knew him to be happy and content.

The sadness which clouded the couple's great happiness was that Patience's attacks of fatigue seemed to grow more frequent, and eventually Richard was forced to the untoward expense of hiring a girl to come in and do what was known as the "rough". It worried Patience that this should happen and it was some weeks before she dared confess that she often sent her hired help to take Dick for an airing while she herself sat drowsily by the fire.

Husbands are notoriously blind to their wives' appearances but soon Richard's friends noticed the change in Patience and, rather naturally, Richard had recourse to the only treatment known to him and he gave Patience a

33

blood-letting every few days—which under the circumstances was the worst possible thing.

On one occasion, when Patience had a severe fainting attack, the maid left the little boy shouting and screaming at the top of his voice, and ran to the shop to bring her master home to attend to his wife. The sight of his dear wife stretched out lifelessly upon the bed, the obvious distress of the maid and the incessant howling of his son, was almost too much for Richard, but he set to work at once and, when Patience began to come out of her faint and look around, the little boy stopped his frightened bawling and the maid, now reassured that her mistress was not dead, resumed her duties. She was a good girl and Richard began to rely upon her more and more to look after Patience and the boy and even to do some of the cooking with outside help for the cleaning.

He was deeply touched to find that Patience, even in her weakness, would insist upon coming downstairs with the assistance of the maid in order to be ready to greet him when he came home, but soon even this became impossible and he went straight upstairs to be with her and try to cheer her.

The glorious sunshine of the past years since Patience came to him had always seemed to be of some dreamlike quality—too beautiful to be real—and now that the clouds of suffering and deep sadness were gathering, Richard found himself unable to accept the inevitable until one unforgettable night, the blow fell. Patience had warded off death until Richard came to her in the evening and then, with his arms around her, she died.

The deep silence in the room was broken by the sobbing of the heartbroken man as he still held the body of his dead wife in his arms. He looked at her in stunned disbelief that she would never speak again—she looked so young and fragile, too young and too good to die. On

34

her finger was the narrow wedding ring which he had so firmly and lovingly placed there. He looked long at it and then slipped it from the thin finger, placed it in a little box and locked it up in a drawer. This action, implying a sense of finality, brought him face to face with the sad reality of his position. With her last words still burning in his heart he went back to the bed and kissed her brow.

From that day Richard Arkwright was a changed man —a light in him was extinguished the night his wife died in his arms. All that was sweet and tender in his nature, his spontaneous humour and gaiety seemed to have been buried with her. Of all people who were hurt by the change, no-one was more affected than his little son who could not understand why his pretty, gay mother was not there to tell him wonderful tales about Robin-a-Bob-bin and his friends. He would sit on his father's knee and play awhile with his watch chain but something had happened to this quiet, staring father who never seemed to respond to his desire for play.

Asthma is a disease which hits you when you are down and Richard was as low in heart as a man can be. His attacks became prolonged and severe and he often had to fight for breath on his way back to the house which was no longer home. He hired a woman to look after the child and left the management of the house to the maid. Instead of hurrying joyfully home to a gay and loving wife and a well-prepared meal at the end of a hard day's work, he now almost dreaded entering the house where, his son asleep upstairs, he could only sit down alone to a cheerless supper. Dick only saw his father at weekends when they would walk hand in hand through the fields where Patience had walked, and Richard, in his fits of abstraction, would get a strange feeling that she was with them. When Dick was five years old the kindly woman who ran the dame-school offered to take him into the school—although really too young—and teach him with methods suited to his age. Dick proved to be a more willing and able scholar than his father had been.

Richard Arkwright was a man of action who, left to himself, tended to be precipitate when once he had made up his mind. His decisions, worked out under the influence of the clearsighted mind of Patience, had been mature and ready for action but now he was on his own and his mind was still clouded by his loss. He bought a public house and equipped it at great expense in the hope that it would make money chiefly, but also to use the extra facilities it afforded with his experiments on cotton machines. It was a complete failure and he lost not only a great deal of capital but, and what was even worse, he began to lose confidence in himself.

But Richard Arkwright was a man who by nature fought back against adversity. His credit was good in Bolton and, although he had lost much of his hard earned and carefully hoarded wealth, he still had a good business and was a master in his craft. He still held the secret formula of his dye and all that it meant in exclusive trade with his richer patrons and, with mind and body fully engaged in hard work and long hours, the sharpness of his great sorrow became dulled and more bearable. It was when he got home at night that his sadness deepened; there was little joy in his house and the long, lonely nights often seemed to be interminable. The very thought of another woman taking the place of Patience appalled him and he tried hard to dismiss it from his mind but without success. He knew that he needed a partner to make his house into a home again and worried long over the problem until the day came when a solution began to seem possible.

36

Mr. Biggins, a highly respected and well-to-do citizen of Leigh, had ordered a wig and, mapping out the day to include delivery of the wig and a tour around the district in search of a fresh supply of hair, Richard set out for the fine house of his customer in the Market Place.

A pert little maid opened the door and conducted him to the parlour informing him on the way that "Master's in t' garden—I'll goo an' fetch 'im."

Left alone and rather disconcerted by the off-hand manner of the maid, he took out the new wig from the box and arranged the hair carefully while he awaited the arrival of his client who soon came in accompanied by a tall, good-looking young woman whom he introduced as his daughter Margaret. The frank, self-assured look on her handsome face as she greeted him as if on terms of equality tended rather to add to his discomfiture and when, looking down at the wig on the table, she exclaimed, "Eh, but yon's a gradely wig—you'll look reet grand in that, won't you, father?" Richard found himself actually belittling the skill for which normally he would have accepted the praise as being well-merited.

Mr. Biggins invited him to stay to dinner. During the meal he noted particularly that on whatever subject whether of cotton, the making of wigs, the state of trade and even of the local need for Sunday Schools, Margaret joined in as an equal and showed that she was as well-informed as the men. It was a new experience for Richard and he found himself enjoying the company as well as he was enjoying the excellent meal set before him. His host and Margaret appeared to be well pleased with him and the meal went so well that they pressed him to come again as their guest. Riding home to Bolton that night he felt within himself a new sense of exhilaration and self-confidence.

Several visits to Leigh followed and on every occasion he found himself admiring more and more the forthright, knowledgeable and self-assured young woman and almost unwillingly he began to think of her as a desirable wife and partner. He felt the need for someone to be at his side at home and in the business, and here was a bonny enough woman who was intelligent, eminently sensible and down-to-earth and with a business sense which he thought remarkable—she also had £400 in her own right. He made up his mind to approach her with a view to marriage.

There was no long and tender wooing, no love letters, no sighs and no pretty vacillation. He seized his opportunity, not without qualms, when he was walking one day with her in the garden. He stopped and faced her. "I suppose," he asked tentatively, "I'm not good enough to ask thee to marry me? Ever since I met thee I have thought there was no other woman with such a quick mind as thine—is a barber good enough for thee to wed, Margaret?"

For a few seconds they stood and looked each other in the face as a soundless dialogue passed between them and then, in complete understanding, they both laughed. "I know a clever chap when I see one," she said, slipping her hand into his, *"And* one who could do wi' the bit o' brass I've got, I shouldn't wonder. Nay, Richard Arkwright, tha's not too humble for me and if tha wants me, tha can have me."

Chapter Four

Margaret—and the Machine

With the willing consent of Mr. Biggins to the marriage, Richard lost no time in taking Margaret over to Bolton for a day to let her see the house in Deansgate and be introduced to his small son. Thence they went to the establishment of the Subterranean Barber where he showed her round the shop and into the back room where he used the secret dye.

It was a successful day. Young Richard and Margaret took an instant liking to each other and Margaret showed an intelligent appreciation of all that he was doing in the business. She understood the circumstances that had led to his recent loss of capital and, with her business acumen, saw that the establishment was worth the injection of her money and would become again a thriving business. It was with a sigh of relief when the examination was over and he was told that he had passed—for that was how it appeared to him—and the plans for the wedding went ahead quickly.

They were married in March 1761 in Leigh and came happily to Bolton where the house had been specially prepared for its new mistress. Young Dick, aged six, and his father settled down once more to a well-regulated and well-kept home and the business, now free from financial strain, soon picked up and began to thrive.

Margaret proved a staunch companion, level headed, a fine manager and devoted to Dick, as he became devoted to her. She was stronger than Patience had ever been even in days of good health, she cared for her house, cooked and baked and then was searching for further occupation.

She suggested that Richard might find her useful at wig-making and every day she followed him down to his underground shop and was quickly initiated into the business.

This was an altogether new idea for Richard, very novel, but extremely useful. Margaret had quick and nimble fingers, manufactured wigs at a greater speed than ever Richard had achieved, and was shown the famous secret of dyeing hair before many weeks had passed.

Bolton thought it a strange sight when husband and wife walked home together from work and were not sure that they approved, but Mrs. Arkwright was a downright, friendly person, and became a familiar figure as she went to and from her husband's business.

Richard was distinctly proud of her; no man had such labour, and for free too! The money continued to roll in; the mess he had got into when he purchased the public house was quite forgotten, the shop in the cellar was given up, and a fine new one in a taking position next to a well-known inn, was bought. He and Margaret were affluent and content.

Money continued to be the ruling passion of his life, and his thrift grew with the years. Since the death of Patience he seemed to lose the jollity of his early youth and his appearance grew more stern and gruff, but underneath he still had a tender heart and a love of human nature; at times it was hidden by a furious temper, which often got the better of him, and although it was of short duration, was devilish while it lasted.

Margaret had a quick temper too, and many were

the blazing rows in the new shop over their work, and in their home, but with both, the rows did not last long, and though at one moment they were shouting at each other, the next they were lovingly reconciled.

"What a tartar thou art!" exclaimed Richard in one of their moments of great mutual affection. "One moment I could beat thee, and not long after, I could forgive thee anything!"

"'Tis the same with me!" said Margaret caressing his cheeks. "Perhaps that's why I do love thee so, because thee does nobbut change. But I wouldn't have thee different; there's none in Lancashire can touch my Richard!" and she kissed him lightly on the brow.

Richard pulled her to him. "I could never have thought I would love a woman again, but I have a proper good mind for thee, my dear, yet carrying my child, thou still has the character of a man!"

"As long as I'm not treated as one!" cried Margaret, and that, thought Richard, was the great difference between her and Patience, who had been like a little girl craving affection, whilst Margaret was bold and strong and drew out the rough side of his nature.

She was so incredibly healthy that it seemed impossible that she should be working almost to the day when their first child was born, barely nine months after their wedding. Richard was delighted and Margaret rather disgusted to find her activities curtailed, but the little girl quickly wound her way into the very depths of Margaret's heart, and she and her mother became very close.

Dick was enchanted to have a baby sister and treated her as some delightful plaything, and as she grew up, Susannah adored him. They were a happy family in an undemonstrative way, except for the flaming tempers of both father and mother, but Dick grew used to this, never thought they meant anything serious, and scarcely remembering his own mother, was very fond of Margaret.

Margaret produced two other daughters who both, to Richard's intense disappointment, died in infancy, but whatever the state of her health, Margaret still continued to work in the barber's shop.

Dick was now apprenticed to Richard as well, but the latter was growing weary of wig making and dyeing and longed to be in the midst of the feverish activity connected with cotton spinning. He "fiddled" as he had always liked to do, of an evening, and his head was reeling with ideas. The Subterranean Barber was watching, listening and playing with thoughts entirely unconnected with wig making, and in his mind was the vague outline of what he called a spinning frame, and for many weeks he planned what was really needed to mechanise the process, though he still lacked the elementary principles of how to make it work.

He and Margaret frequently went over to Leigh to visit her many relatives, and there, there was much talk of curious goings-on behind closed doors, and of machines being made which were about to revolutionise the cotton industry.

Near Margaret's home lived a man named Thomas Highs with his wife and daughter Jane. Highs had a mechanical turn of mind and the Biggins family were certain something was afoot in a room at the top of his house, which, the maids whispered, was always kept locked, and where Highs was closeted for hours with a watchmaker named Kay.

Richard's inquisitiveness was aroused.

Highs spoke of his machine as his "jenny" after his daughter but he and Kay did not persevere with an invention they could not perfect, and there were days when nothing was done.

"He's a clever chap that Kay," said Mr. Biggins as he talked to Richard over Sunday dinner. "Clever with making wheels and such like, in fact I'd say proper smart, but what they two be up to, I can only guess, though I reckon it's to do with a spinning machine."

"That's what's wanted," said Richard eagerly. "We won't get nowhere with weaving cotton material while there's such a shortage of yarn, and the industry don't get no help from the wool people."

The Yorkshire wool merchants were indeed protected by Act of Parliament and were bitterly against any mechanisation of cotton spinning.

"Well I'll be damned if Highs has got the brains to make a spinning machine," said Biggins decisively. "And anyway it won't be much thought of by folks as spin by hand. Mark my words, if it ever did come to something, there'd be a rare spot of bother in Lancashire.

Richard agreed, but his great interest was aroused, and on their next visit to Leigh, he and Margaret were told that one night, Highs and Kay in a fit of despondency and temper, had thrown the machine out of the window as being quite unworkable, and that Highs' wife who had disapproved of the whole project, was delighted.

Everyone in Leigh thought it the joke of a lifetime—especially the spinners, who saw the threat to their cottage industry as past and over.

"And Highs called it his 'jenny' after his daughter!" they chortled. "A jenny! That'll teach him not to go mucking abaht with what don't concern him!"

But Richard Arkwright sat at home and thought very deeply as he played with his amateur spinning frame in the evenings.

He was not enough of a mechanic to complete his project, but he remembered Kay, and one of the big decisions of his life was taken.

Highs shut himself up in his house nursing his disappointment, but Kay was so upset that he left Leigh for Warrington, determined to cut aloof from the scene of his failure. It did not take Richard long to seek him out.

He journeyed to Warrington, made no mention of Highs' fateful invention and asked Kay's help over some trivial matters of wheels and wires. Kay was no inventor and simply worked to order. He liked Richard and when matters had gone a little further, Richard told him that although he had no wish to steal Highs' idea, yet he had some thought that it could be incorporated in the frame which he had been attempting to put together.

"I'll pay you well if you'll do some weeks' work for me," said Richard largely, but he meant what he said. Kay was a smart wheel cutter, Richard paid handsomely for his services, and left him to work on his own.

Richard was cunning enough to discover all he could of what was going on in the cotton industry; he went about asking questions with the tenacity which was his great characteristic, and knowing how occupied his mind was, Margaret was flabbergasted when he suggested taking a couple of days off and going to the races at Kersal Moor in Manchester.

"What's bitten thee?" she enquired suspiciously. "'Tis not like thee to go gallivanting!"

Richard looked down at his feet unwilling to meet her eyes.

"I've heard summut," he said. "There are two chaps called Wyatt and Paul what made something like I have in mind with my spinning frame; I'm told that Wyatt will be at the races, and I thought I'd like to have a word with him."

"I thought there was summut behind this!" said Margaret. "Thee don't need to cover up that much, Richard!

You go if you want, but I'd advise thee not to poke thy nose into a lot of rubbish, and I'll have nought to do with it! A waste of time I call it."

Undeterred, Richard arranged with Kay to take a small model of his frame to Manchester; he knew that the patent had lapsed on Wyatt and Paul's machine and that it had failed lamentably in all the places where it had been tried out, but he was anxious to discover if his own invention was in any way like the one which had been made and discarded.

He already had a slight contempt for both men for giving up so readily, but he wanted to explore every avenue before he risked going further with his own model.

Visiting a racecourse was a new experience and he knew nothing about it, but he was astounded to meet a great number of his clients, and enjoyed quite a welcome. It had never entered his head to take time off for enjoyment of such a chancy nature and he was still more astounded to find Wyatt, instead of being a dispirited man, was betting light-heartedly, and apparently none the worse for having failed with his invention.

Richard suddenly realised that his own life was nothing but one hard slog and that there was another side to existence of which he was completely ignorant; now he was among a crowd of men who, though hard workers, knew how to enjoy themselves with the hearty jollity of the north country.

He searched out Wyatt who was only mildly interested in his idea and did not hesitate to warn Richard that there was really no future in any invention to mechanise spinning but suggested in the friendliest possible manner that the whole thing was better left alone.

It astounded Richard that he appeared to have

accepted failure so easily, but having chatted to him in an extremely casual way, he managed to pick up a few hints and went straight back to Kay in Warrington, ordering him to set to work on a second model.

A jenny had been made by a man called Hargreaves, a great improvement on the one cast away by Highs, but it had not as yet upset the spinners, for it could be used in their cottage homes and enabled them to work with a greater number of spindles at one time; Richard's idea was on a larger scale and, if only he could achieve success, would revolutionise the entire cotton industry.

He knew that his machine was far ahead of anything which had been tried before, but men were experimenting on all sides and the workers knew that their home trade was being threatened. Richard was frankly scared to try out his experiments in Bolton, where suspicions were rife, and determined to make a trip to Preston, where he had some family and many friends, and discover if he could perfect his invention there, for Preston was far enough away to be undisturbed by the cotton agitators.

But first he had to settle with Margaret.

For some weeks their altercations had been waging fast and furious; all she could see was Richard's complete neglect of his profitable business and his constant preoccupation with the miniature models supplied to him by Kay and carefully shut away in a cupboard in a locked room. They meant nothing to her and she was convinced that Richard was giving up the substance of a good concern to follow some illusory dream and it infuriated her.

When he announced that he proposed to go to Preston for a few weeks "on business", she flew off the handle.

"Have you gone mad, Richard Arkwright?" she screamed at him. "What do you propose doing with the shop, I'd like to know! That man Kay with his wheels, has gone to thy head! Don't tell me you're going to be another Highs, because I won't stand for it!"

"I've an idea better'n he had," growled Richard. "And I don't want folks to know; that's why I'm going to Preston, where I'll be right away from all this talk and people prying."

"Prying indeed!" hissed Margaret, looking at the models on the table of the room to which he had admitted her. "Who'd want to pry at all this clobber? You'd better mind your own job, which you haven't done of late, and the shop isn't what it used to be. You mark my words! We'll all be in Queer Street if you carry on like this, and you a man with two children, not to mention a wife! I got you out of one mess when I married you, and I'm not going to get you out of another!"

Richard hated her for those words; the one thing he could not stand was to be reminded of his failure with the public house.

"All I ask is that thee'll trust me," he pleaded, trying to bite back a spate of angry words. "I shan't be gone long, but I'd like to have a chance to get going with the frame."

"Gone long!" shouted Margaret. "You won't be gone at all if I can help it! You and your useless crocks!"

Beside herself with fury and before Richard realised what was in her mind, she had seized some of the models and thrown them through the window, where they clattered, bent and broken, on the stone paving of the yard.

Richard saw red; he boxed her ears in fury and rushed down the stairs to see what he could retrieve, while Margaret snatched several other models, hurried to the kitchen grate and thrust them into the fire.

47

Margaret's action made him more fiercely determined than ever to go on with his project and, while she in her turn locked herself into her room, he picked up his models and tried to repair the damage.

This was the worst quarrel they had ever had and, before either thought of repentance, Richard had hurried off to Warrington once more, collected part of the finished frame, and forwarded it to Preston.

Only then did he return home. Margaret was in tears, full of self-recrimination and after a half-hearted scene of reconciliation, promised that she and Dick and a journeyman named Dean, would continue to run the business in Bolton, if Richard would promise not to be too long away.

Richard felt disloyal to Margaret as he took young Dick on one side and tried to explain why he was leaving Bolton and starting something which his wife considered a wild goose chase, and Dick was sympathetic.

He knew well enough the talk in Lancashire and the public grumbling of the spinners; he was fired by the dream that his own father might have found the answer to some of these mechanical failures which had up to now been so disastrous.

"We'll be all right in the shop," he said comfortingly. "Don't bother about it; the frame is certainly worth a try, for supposing it were a success, wig-making would be nothing in comparison!"

Encouraged by Dick's co-operation, Richard took coach to Preston, thinking long thoughts as he crossed the open moorland, of the far-off days when he had walked to Bolton for the first time and been told of Mr. Pollitt who might want an assistant.

His family—what was left of them—and his old friends with whom he had chased light-heartedly through the streets, gave him a warm welcome, and

48

though curious as to what had brought him back to his own town, were satisfied with an explanation that it was something to do with the manufacture of clocks.

Only to an extreme few whom he knew he could trust, did he confide what was the real object of his visit, and even those few were not particularly excited by his disclosures. Preston was very far from East Lancashire, and the question of cotton manufacture was not of such burning interest.

A room was hired, the first part of the frame installed, and hot on his employer's heels came Kay, the only man admitted to the secret room. He worked out Richard's idea of two rollers to be joined by toothed wheels, and it looked as if success were in sight, but questions began to be asked; the so-called clock maker had been thirteen weeks in Preston, and it seemed suspicious to outsiders that any clock should take so long to perfect.

Early in the year 1768, Richard Arkwright with his spinning frame ready to be tried out, found himself in terribly low water. All these weeks Kay had been paid good wages, and now Richard's pockets were depleted.

Margaret wrote depressing accounts of the barber's shop, and even young Dick who had always backed his father, was sent to Preston to try and bring home to him the very serious financial situation in which the family were now placed.

"There's not much coming in the way of brass," he explained in his most grown-up tone. "But Mother thinks you should return and see what you can do to pull the business round. She says you've got to think of her and Susannah, and she don't seem to be getting anywhere without you."

Richard was desperately worried. His frame was ready except for final trials and adjustments, and he felt that at long last, here was something really good. It would be

49

heart-breaking if, at this stage, he were to abandon his efforts and return to Bolton with his tail between his legs.

"Tell Mother to give me another week or two," he almost pleaded with Dick. "Then if nought comes of it, I'll come back."

He was reduced to selling some of his clothes and any oddments he could get hold of, in order to send Dick home with a little ready cash. He could no longer blame Margaret for the furious letters she wrote to him and his spirits were at a low ebb. As always, at such moments of worry in his life, he was plagued with violent attacks of asthma, which only served to increase his deep depression.

But tenacity was the mainspring of his character; a little thing like the temporary shortage of money was not going to deter his final efforts.

He turned to a friend of his, John Smalley, and hating the position of beggar, asked for a loan.

Smalley had great faith in Richard; he was disturbed by rumours of rioting in East Lancashire among the prosperous spinners, who were terrified at the thought of any new invention, but he backed Richard, not only with cash, but by prevailing on a schoolmaster friend to lend the parlour of the Grammar School house, where surreptitiously, Richard and Kay could erect the spinning frame.

Not even the schoolmaster knew what was going on in his own parlour. Rumours grew, and two old ladies living near by, were frightened by the strange humming noises which came from the house, and were convinced that they were caused by evil spirits.

It suited Richard that this particular story should be spread abroad; he acted up to it, pulled his hat over his eyes and turned up his coat collar whenever he went out, hoping that he looked both furtive and sinister.

People were terrified of the supernatural and to his great delight, passed the house quickly with averted eyes, and he was left in peace.

But at last the spinning frame was working, joined to a jenny much on the lines which Highs and Kay had thrown through the window, and was spinning twist on twenty spindles where before only two at a time could be done by hand.

Poor as he now was, and worried to death at the news of the hard times to which he had brought his family, Richard applied for the patent rights on his machine.

Hargreaves' invention made it possible to work eight spindles from one wheel and the output was enormously increased without any disruption in the lives of working people. They could still live as they always had done, working their own hours and slipping out to dig in their gardens whenever they felt inclined, but Arkwright's spinning frame and jenny demanded the construction of a factory and the beginning of a new way of life, which was utterly foreign.

Lancashire seethed with anxiety. There had been Wyatt and Paul who had started the rot, although they had failed in their efforts; there was Highs who had another go at Leigh; there was Hargreaves, and now there was Arkwright who was obviously up to no good.

Serious rioting began at Stanhill; several of Hargreaves' machines were smashed to pieces by the mob, who were encouraged by middle-class people fearing mass unemployment and an increase in the poor rates.

"Trade is in danger!" was the cry. "The bread of the honest poor is to be taken from their mouths! Down with all machines and with any traitor who invented them!"

Hargreaves not only had his jennies destroyed but his house also and he hurriedly moved to Nottingham where all was quiet.

It is a strange thought that the rioters did all they could to impede the progress of inventions which later on ended by giving employment to thousands and bringing prosperity to the whole country.

It was not only unemployment but a way of life which was threatened; factory life in the future was a hard business and, looking back across the span of two centuries, one wonders if the older and simpler existence did not bring greater happiness and peace of mind than the era of great prosperity with less and less freedom.

Richard was frankly scared of starting work in Bolton; he could not bear the thought that the same fate might await him which had destroyed Hargreaves, and backed by his faithful old friend Smalley, he took the tremendous decision to leave everything that was familiar to him and make a new start in the Nottingham area.

He dreaded having to return to Bolton and breaking the news to Margaret. He knew the terrible scene that would ensue, and he was a little frightened of what Dick would think of it all, but his journey back was an essential preliminary to the family upheaval.

He took the coach home and Margaret was deeply upset to see Richard in his shabby clothes, grown much thinner, and in the midst of a severe attack of asthma as he walked into the Deansgate house.

"Sit down and have your dinner before you tell us what brings you back," she said kindly. Dinner was on the table, the fire glowed brightly, Susannah was enchanted to see her father again and insisted on sitting on his knee whilst he ate, and for a moment Richard almost lacked courage to speak of his new plan.

The house was so full of memories—happy ones of the years of his life with Patience, the background of his big success as a barber and wig-maker, the birthplace of both Dick and Susannah, and here he was proposing to break every tie and start on an unknown adventure, with no capital and only the generosity of Smalley to help him at the start.

As the meal was finished and cleared away, so the tension mounted in the Arkwright living-room.

At last Richard schooled himself into speaking.

"We're going to move," he said in an extra loud voice in order to give himself the semblance of courage and decision. "The machine is working, and now I must get started with making more of them, and maybe spinning myself."

There was a horrified silence.

"Why've we got to move?" breathed Margaret quietly, as if she were gathering strength for a major attack later on. "What's wrong with Bolton?"

"Everything's wrong with Bolton!" Richard continued to shout. "What with riots and troubles and people saying they'll smash every machine made, 'tis no place for the likes of us what has got something really good to get on its feet."

"And how d'you know it's good?" queried Margaret. "You've seen the mess Highs made; you know those two chaps in Manchester did no good with their contraption, and folks say that Hargreaves at Stanhill has had all his machines smashed to pieces."

"I *know* mine's good," said Richard with iron determination. "And that's why we must get out to some place where folks is ignorant about spinning cotton. Hargreaves has gone to Nottingham and Smalley, who has faith in my frame, says he'll come with us to somewhere in the Midlands and help us get started."

"And what about the business here in Bolton?" said Margaret, still in her ominously quiet voice.

"Well, from what Dick tells me, it's not in any great shape, and won't be all that loss," said Richard doggedly.

There was a long silence.

"When you talk of 'us' going," said Margaret, "you can't include me, Richard Arkwright." Her voice was taut with anger. "I've worked for you for eight long years, and lately without either sight or sound of you, and I'm right fed up!"

"I cannot do without thee and Dick," said Richard brokenly.

"I'll come, Father," said Dick. "You've gone this far and it wouldn't be right to look back now."

"You'll move without me," said Margaret furiously. "No man could have had a wife that has done more for him than I have for you; slaved, I have, and now no thanks, but only an order to up-sticks and leave our home."

"I don't order thee, I only ask," said Richard, his adventurous ambitions marred by a sudden feeling of shame. "It'd mean a lot to me to have all my family with me, because it's a great thing we may be doing."

"You and your great things!" scoffed Margaret. "I'll believe them when I see them, but I'm staying put, or taking Susannah to some smaller place, but come with you—NO."

The mention of Susannah was a cruel cut of the whip, but Richard knew there was no question of separating the little girl from her mother. "I do beg thee to come," he said humbly, and for once he entirely controlled his fiery temper. "I know this thing is going to be the biggest success in England, and one day, thee'll be right proud to have helped me with the start of it."

"Don't talk to me about helping you with the start!" shouted Margaret. "I'd like to know what you think I've been doing with the shop and all! Haven't I worked for you for months? and all I see is a man coming back with clothes scarce fit to cover his body, and no brass to call his own! You can go with your jenny and the spinning frame and see where they'll get you! And you can sell the business and this house too, and I'll thank you to give me the brass they fetch. Any road, you're no good to me!" and she flung out of the room, went quickly upstairs and firmly locked her bedroom door.

"Well, I reckon that's that!" said Richard bitterly to Dick. "One day I'll ride in my own carriage but never with her beside me, and not for her am I giving up the idea of Nottingham. We're on to summut good, lad, and I thank thee for sticking by me."

"I don't like the idea of the family splitting," said Dick gloomily. "Mother and I have always got on well, and I can't bear the thought of leaving the little one."

"That hurts," said Richard tersely. "But I've put my hand to the plough and I'm not turning back."

The next week was not pleasant. Margaret hardly spoke, except when absolutely necessary; the business of selling the barber's business was put in train, so was the disposal of the Deansgate house; Richard picked out some necessary furniture for himself and Dick, and in a very short time had removed to Hockley, outside Nottingham.

Susannah was too young to know what it all meant, but was pleasantly excited with the prospect of a new home somewhere quite different, and whether it was Nottingham or back to her mother's old house in Leigh, did not matter. She scarcely realised that Dick was no longer going to be part of her daily life and was comforted by Richard telling her that she would often come to visit them both.

Margaret pursed her lips and said nothing, but in the future she never raised any objection to Susannah visiting her father.

55

Richard gave all that he could in the way of money to his wife and found that the breaking up of his family life meant little or nothing compared to the intense excitement ahead.

The great machine was moved by road from Preston, Kay going with it to act as mechanic, and Smalley followed, but before any golden prospects opened, there was a long and hard battle to be fought.

Chapter Five

The Machine

Here was a deep and unbridgeable clash of wills. Margaret, the woman, could not see any reason why a successful business—to which she had materially contributed both in money and in work—and a good home should all be sacrificed to an elusive and uncertain contraption to be used in the textile industry which was, in any case, nothing to do with her husband's trade. His obsession with the machine was bringing his legitimate business to ruin and this caused her both anger and dismay. Richard, on the other hand, had pursued his single-minded aim of perfecting the machine in which he had such confidence and was prepared to resist all efforts from whatever source, to turn him from it.

In April 1768 he moved with his machine to Nottingham where Smalley was prepared to back his invention but refused to foot the bill for food and lodging for the workers.

Richard found a suitable place in which a large upper room could house the machine and serve as a bedroom for the three men and the ground floor rooms could be used as a barber's shop. Kay was not satisfied with this lowly accommodation and lodged in more respectable quarters nearby and his place was taken in the workshop dormitory by an extra assistant named Wood. Richard and his son opened up the shop and worked at the one trade in which they were both expert and whatever money they earned over and above their minimum needs was spent on the frame upstairs.

Young Dick who, in his youth and enthusiasm, expected quick results became at times gloomy and despondent but his father, with perhaps more optimism that even he felt, would say, "You just wait, lad. I *know* I'm on to a good thing but it all takes time and we've got to put up wi' a bit o' discomfort until we finish the job. This idea o' Wood's about fluting the rollers is a gradely one and well worth the extra time an' cost. Bear up, son! Success is in sight now and we'll both on us look back to these days wi' the satisfaction of a job well done."

"It's alright for Kay," grumbled Dick. "He always knows he's got his wages coming to him, but it seems as if you get the thick end of the stick, looking after us all and always with Mr. Smalley peering over your shoulder."

"He's been a good friend," answered Richard quietly. I don't know where I'd be without him and you, for there's nobody else has any faith in me, but twelve months from now, it will be a different story I can promise you."

He and Dick worked harder than they had ever done before at their barbering, but Richard never ceased to think and dream of cotton spinning, and often, when a sudden idea came to him, he would rush upstairs leaving a customer half-covered with soap suds, call to Dick to come to his aid, and spend the next few hours tinkering with his wheels and wires.

Often in the night, he would jump from his bed and by the light of a candle start fiddling about whilst Dick, worn out with trying to do the work of his father and himself, would sleep like the dead.

It was a very different life from the one in Bolton where Margaret gave them all a comfortable home, where Dick could go out on a summer evening and play the newly invented game of cricket with other lads of his own age, or in the winter sit at home by the blazing fire after a splendidly fulfilling supper, and Susannah would bring out the spillikins and challenge him to a match.

Nottingham was hardly gay, for nobody bothered with the unknown barber and his son, and Richard was chary of making friends who might conceivably want to know the secrets of his spinning frame.

Dick amused himself by catching eels in the river during the long summer evenings and even hooked a salmon on one rare and memorable occasion but he was often very bored and homesick, as was his father, for they both hated the mean conditions under which they lived. Richard could not help feeling at times that he had brought this sadness on those he loved by his own self-will and pride and he often longed for the comforts of home and a reconciliation with Margaret but he was determined to see the frame working and that meant he stayed in Nottingham. To help Dick, and possibly because he was hungry for news of home, he sent Dick to stay with Margaret and Susannah for a holiday while he wrestled with the remaining problems in the frame and, at last, came complete success. The Machine worked!

Now followed some months of strenuous but exciting effort. The Patent was applied for and granted and Smalley, now satisfied that the machine was a viable investment, kept his promise and provided the capital for the business. A small mill was bought in 1769 and the horse powered machine installed and set to work. It was a testing time for them all. The outlay necessary to get the mill into production had all but exhausted Smalley's available funds. Little by little as production increased, the money began to come in until the first profits on the business were made and, from that time, it became increasingly successful.

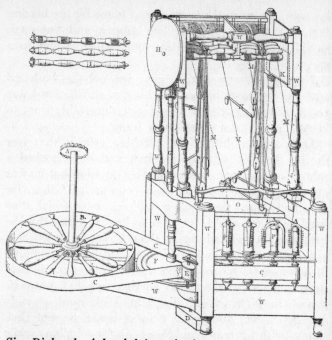

Sir Richard Arkwright's spinning machine, patented
1769

Richard was jubilant and in his enthusiasm his
ambition tended to run when the business was still only
walking. He began to press Smalley for more and more
capital for bigger and better mills where with greater
expansion and more output they could not fail to grow
wealthy but Smalley preferred to walk steadily before he
attempted to run and was very reluctant to dig deeper
into his purse.

"I'm getting tired of what you call 'tiding you over',"
he said shortly to Richard. "I've done all I can for you
and still you're after more brass; in fact, I'm not going
on any longer and you can look somewhere else for your

capital. I don't believe in the amount you say is needed."

By this time Richard's temper was wearing very thin; he was working until he nearly fell asleep on his feet, his products were successful, and now suddenly Smalley was planning to leave him in the lurch. Thankful as he was for all that Smalley had done, his quick temper overcame him, and he rounded on his old friend.

"Nobody can say that I'm not grateful," he thundered, "But to leave me high and dry is a bitter pill. If you haven't got the brass there's no more to be said, but you're leaving me just as we're launched on the road to success, and it may well be the end of me and good-bye to your money, for unless I get some help now, I'm through."

"If you're through it serves you right," said Smalley angrily. "I've yet to meet a more strong-headed, persistent beggar than you are, and the minute money starts to come in, it's the old story—'I must have this to tide me over', 'We must spend a bit more in order to get this, that or t' other done'; it never seems to end. Anyway you've had the last penny from me; I don't like Nottingham, nor ever will, and I'll be glad to see the last of it and get me back to Preston."

Richard could not even bring himself to say that he was sorry; he felt completely broken at the thought that he must abandon the success which had already started to arrive.

The two old friends parted in a sad and angry mood, and it was only to Dick that Richard dared confess that he was on the verge of failure.

What made it harder was the prosperity which surrounded them, for Nottingham was the centre of the hosiery trade, working to capacity in every sphere, and no one took any notice of the small mill which housed an almost untried machine.

But Richard took his courage in both hands and decided to try his luck with the banker Ichabod Wright.

By now his wardrobe was so diminished that he had hard work to look respectable enough to present himself at the Bank, but he never lacked courage, and Mr. Wright was impressed enough by the stocky Lancashire man to make enquiries, and decided to give him a helping hand, provided the Bank could have half the profits made.

This stuck in Richard's gullet, for he knew from the short experience he had had of manufacturing his machine that for some time the profits were likely to be remarkably small, and he was not altogether surprised some weeks later, when Mr. Wright sent for him with a grave face, and told him that the return on their money was not good enough for any Bank.

"I'm sorry," he said kindly, for he had grown to like Richard with his palpable enthusiasm and honesty. "But I am afraid that we must bring our partnership to a close. However I wish you very well and it might be of interest to both of you, to meet a customer of ours, Samuel Need, who is a decidedly prosperous business man, and might well find your invention of some use."

It was something which Richard had to accept with as good a grace as he could muster, but he set his teeth and determined that he would have yet another try and see what Samuel Need could do for him.

Once again he went cap in hand, a role which did not suit him, and found that Need was readier to listen than the Bank had been and suggested that he had a partner called Jedediah Strutt who was something of a mechanic himself, and might like the idea of the spinning frame for which there was such acute need and which no one else had been able to construct successfully.

Strutt, a man six years younger than Richard, had

originally been a farmer, but with his aptitude for mechanics, he had become interested in the hosiery business and was well-known as the inventor of a machine which made the famous "Derby rib" stockings. He had a clear, cool intellect, was an extremely kindly man and full of the same type of energy which motivated Richard.

Samuel Need, on the other hand, was hard-headed, critical and very cautious in his approach to any new project but Strutt convinced him that the machine had wonderful potentials and that, if the three of them combined, they were on to something really promising. Richard could hardly believe in his good fortune especially when he found how ready they were to back his enterprise with what seemed to him to be unlimited capital and he used it to the full.

Another and larger mill was bought and equipped with the new frames and the success of the venture delighted him and his partners. He and his son had long abandoned the mean and spartan life which they had been forced by sheer necessity to endure in the upper room and the barber's shop below, for better quarters. Now with his new success, he and Dick occupied a comfortable house together with servants to wait on them. Once more they enjoyed the delights of good furniture and well-made, sober dress which they had almost forgotten existed, and began to mix with the rich hosiery manufacturers of the district on an equal footing.

Dick, who had stuck by his father during the hard and lean days of their struggle, was overwhelmed by this sudden and dramatic change in their fortunes.

Now he had money of his own to spend, good food, good clothes and a comfortable home to live in, but he was allowed no relaxation, and every working day he accompanied his father to the new mill at five o'clock in the morning without fail before the mill-hands arrived, and worked hard throughout the long day. Now and again he would grumble about this to Richard but the reply came only too quickly—"You came into this world to work, lad, and when you've done a few more years at it you can begin to think of enjoyment." Yet he felt sorry for the lad, who still sadly missed his home and whenever possible, would go for a couple of days to Margaret's house in Leigh, where Susannah was growing up into a pretty child.

She kept asking when she might come to visit them in Nottingham, but Dick knew that engrossed as his father was, even the arrival of his only little daughter would prove too much for him and the child would be left for many hours alone.

"Would you not bring her?" he asked Margaret. "We've got a fine house now and you'd like being comfortable." But he said it without great conviction, because he knew how sore Richard was that Margaret had destroyed his models and deserted him at a time in his life which had proved unbelievably hard and difficult.

"Your father and I don't see eye to eye," said Margaret. "He can come and see Susannah whenever he has a mind to, but she's too young to go that far and be left to the care of maid servants; she's better and happier with me."

"I'd fetch her and bring her back," said Dick pleadingly. "But I can't say about my father. He works harder than you'd believe possible, and if he goes on as he's started, he'll soon be a right rich man."

"That makes no difference to me," said Margaret haughtily. "Wealth is of the heart and not the pocket, and it's many a long year since your father put his family before his work, and I don't forget it."

"I think he'd be glad to see you," said Dick lamely, but even now he realised that his family were far from coming first in Richard's life, and that nothing would tear him from his mills.

Richard was permanently seeking after further spoils.

In his youth he had heard of a man in Derby who had worked his silk mill by water wheels, and he saw immense possibilities for the spinning frame if something of the same sort could be done.

Ever since his early days in Bolton when a horse had been given to him by his barber employer, he had loved riding, and now he went far afield from Nottingham on Sundays when the mills were closed, looking for a spot near water where yet more factories could be erected.

The nearby county of Derbyshire is one of the most varied and beautiful in England; there are wild stretches of moorland where the only inhabitants are sheep and grouse; there are rushing rivers in deep valleys, steep grassy fields and grey stone walls, and there is also a countryside of park-like pasture land with fine trees.

It is a county of legend and history, of stories of Friar Tuck and Robin Hood who came over from Sherwood Forest, of the romance of Dorothy Vernon of Haddon Hall, and of the river Dove, where Izaak Walton fished and wrote his *Compleat Angler*.

Richard Arkwright was fascinated by it and deeply impressed by some of the great houses of which Chatsworth, the home of the Duke of Devonshire, was the most splendid of them all. He loved the solid little grey stone cottages too, the towering limestone cliffs and the contrast between desolate, wild country and quiet meadowlands.

Often he would stay away for a night and travel a greater distance, and eventually he found a site which he

C.A.—E

considered perfect, at the tiny hamlet of Cromford, where the waters of the Derwent were joined by Bonsall brook, and he rode up and down the river banks, prospecting and seeing in his mind's eye what he could do with this lovely corner of Derbyshire. Here were two sites, one an old corn mill and one a disused paper mill, the only disadvantage being the lack of communications, for the roads were both bad and inadequate, used mainly by pack mules, but otherwise it had the makings of an ideal spot.

The valley was deep, there was a wealth of beautiful trees, and the water coursed among rough grey boulders, forming deep pools and rushing falls. It was a picturesque place with wide meadows and a great quietness after the stinking streets of Nottingham.

Time and again Richard rode over to Cromford planning and dreaming dreams, and when at length he went to his two partners and told them of his idea of a factory in the depths of the country and of the construction of a town to house the workers, he was almost startled at their ready acceptance of it.

It was a revolutionary move, but Richard with his vision of the future, had little difficulty in persuading them it was the right one to make, and it says much for their trust and confidence in him, that the scheme materialised.

Need was inclined to distrust Richard's real reason for removal, saying that he was tired of the narrow-minded, austere, and chapel-loving inhabitants of Nottingham and wished to be among the "county folk" who owned large estates, but he was bound to admit that the whole idea of erecting mills on the banks of a river had a sound commercial basis.

At any rate the venture was a most astonishing success. Not only did Richard build a mill without any architectural assistance, but he built an entire town as well—row upon row of sturdy cottages lining clean, cobbled streets, with shops to meet the needs of the workers, and eventually there was a market and a public house, and for the children, a free school, so that the whole community was complete.

Lookers-on at first thought it was a wild scheme, but it took England by surprise and workers flocked to Cromford because the wages offered were higher than in any city.

The quiet Derbyshire dale was transformed; orders for the water frame, as it was now called, came from all over the world and the mills worked night and day.

As one shift of workers poured out through the gates of an evening, so another was waiting to take over, and as darkness fell, the mill was brilliantly lit by hundreds of candles and the hum of machinery scarcely ceased.

Hardly was the first factory in production, than a second and far larger one was built; further cottages had to be constructed, and eventually as the years passed, mills sprang up throughout Derbyshire, Lancashire, in Nottingham and in Staffordshire.

Richard had an unpretentious but comfortable house near to his first mill, Need built an imposing mansion, and Strutt moved to Belper, where the cotton industry rapidly spread.

The wealth of the three partners grew to enormous proportions, but Richard never knew what it was to slacken his activities, and as he grew older, so his energies seemed to increase.

He moved to Rock House, which was a large gentleman's residence still near to his factories, but whose windows looked down the meadows where the Derwent flowed, but in spite of the opulence in which he lived, the beginning of each day started for him before six o'clock, when he would spend an hour at grammar and reading, and another hour at night, studying writing and spelling; numberless times he regretted that he had not spent more time at night-school in Preston as his uncle had wished, because his illiteracy was a great handicap, but latterly Dick stepped in and wrote most of his letters for him, for correspondence was the greatest headache of all.

His own success startled Richard and never in his wildest dreams had he foreseen anything such as he had now accomplished.

Need was the sceptical partner, as Richard wished to expand further and further. Need wanted them to rest on their laurels with the wonderful success at Cromford and the fact that the water-frame was being used for the manufacture of stockings, but Richard was intent on building yet another factory in Derby for the weaving of calico, and this was an extra worry.

"Success has gone to Arkwright's head," he complained bitterly to Strutt. "He will land us both in a mess if he tries to go on expanding."

Strutt was far more loyal to Richard, but even he became a little distrustful of continual new enterprises and wondered where Richard would stop.

"Who does he think he is anyhow?" went on Need. "Beginning to mix with all the people in the country hereabouts. After all, where did he come from? and who has helped him to the position where he is now?"

Probably Need was jealous because Richard was popular with his employees and had been "taken up" by the county folk, who not only liked him as a rough diamond with his strong Lancashire accent, but were ready to acknowledge the great prosperity he had brought to the region which had up to the time of his coming, been a poor agricultural district.

Highs, who had the moral support of many manufacturers who believed that he had been greatly wronged, was his greatest enemy. He was at work perfecting a double jenny and when he was satisfied that it was ready to put on the market he had it on exhibition in Manchester in 1772. This, of all centres of the industry, was most antagonistic to Richard Arkwright partly out of envy at his great success, and partly because they were convinced that he had stolen the invention from Highs and built his cotton empire on what had never belonged to him.

In the full knowledge of his unpopularity—and partly, perhaps, because of it—Richard Arkwright drove to Manchester in his splendid carriage to inspect the machine. Highs greeted him with a scowl when he saw the equipage and its prosperous owner and, in a voice which carried to those around him, exclaimed, "I should a' been where you are now!"

Richard made no reply but passed on his way and the incident would have ended there but, unfortunately, that evening Richard's hostess, Mrs. Jackson, had included Highs in her invitations, hoping to bring about a reconciliation between the two men at her table. The atmosphere during the meal was electric. Highs could hardly speak a civil word to anyone but just glowered across at Arkwright who exasperated him even more by his calm air of power and prosperity.

At last he could bear it no longer and burst out angrily: "You're using my invention and there's not a shadow of doubt about it!" and he banged his fist on the table, to the consternation of poor Mrs. Jackson.

She had wondered if Richard could not perhaps do something to help Highs, who was in poor circumstances, for unsuccessful or not, he had certainly been a pioneer of cotton spinning machinery.

Richard looked up and his eyes sparkled dangerously.

"Be that as it may," he said quietly. "You had nought to do with my water frame, and if you're still thinking of that jenny of yours, well, if a man invents a thing and does not proceed with it, then others are at liberty to take it up."

It was certainly an admission, but nobody except Richard had had the tenacity to go through fire and water to achieve his object, suffering many hardships and working without ceasing, and he considered himself blameless, for his machine was a triumph of skill and practically a unique invention.

"I'll get even with you yet!" threatened Highs, and Richard, red in the face with anger, rose abruptly from the table and asked that his carriage might be ordered at once.

"Oh dear! Oh, dear!" cried Mrs. Jackson, flushed and uncomfortable, rising with him. "It's my fault for trying to bring you both together! Mr. Arkwright, I wouldn't have had this happen for the world, and now what can I do to mend matters?"

"He don't worry me!" said Richard grandly. "Let him do what he likes: there's nought can touch me now!"

Mrs. Jackson was in tears as she said good-bye to this famous man whom she had been so proud to ask to her house.

"Now what have I started?" she asked herself, returning to the disgruntled Highs, and the evening passed in a shower of bitter invective from him, who from that moment onwards, was fired by only one thought, to discredit his adversary.

There was now tremendous agitation against the new machines, which seemed to be the final death blow to those spinners who worked in their own homes; Lancashire as well as Derbyshire now had to contend with them, and the spinners foresaw the complete redundancy

70

of their cottage industry. Hundreds of them seethed with
anger and a flaming ardour to preserve the old way of
life.

"The jennies are in the hands of the poor, and the
patent machines in the hands of the rich!" was their cry.

Richard and his associates became the arch enemies of
the textile world; people forgot the huge expansion of
the cotton trade and refused to understand what were
the possibilities ahead, turning their wrath on the mill
owners, who they were convinced would be the cause of
mass unemployment.

Chapter Six

Success

The great industrialists of the eighteenth century were
men like Richard Arkwright who, by prodigious labour
business acumen and talent in their particular industry
rose from their lowly beginnings to positions of wealth
and power in the nation, while everyone, from whatever station in life, knew that there were "two nations"
in the country the impact upon people varying accord-
ing to their own personal position. The poor knew that
the rich upper classes existed and accepted the
inevitable distinctions, but the men who won their
wealth like Richard Arkwright, found themselves ever
wealthier than their county neighbours of the upper
classes and yet not even accepted as equals. The barrier
of class was insurmountable in spite of wealth, and
money could not buy a place among the élite.

While, as we have seen, Richard Arkwright himself
was accepted with admiration and respect by the county
he rarely found time even to visit them and certainly
not to indulge himself in their elegant idleness. Dick, on
the other hand, was young, handsome and rich and an
ornament in any situation. In his fashionable dress-silk
coat laced with gold, satin knee breeches and hair tied
back with a large bow—he had all the appearance of
being "a native here and to the manner born" and
Richard was glad that the time had come, as he had
promised, when his son could enjoy himself. Glad and
proud, too, to see how well Dick was being accepted in

the local mansions of the county—even to the greatest of them all at Chatsworth.

Dick found himself in a strange world. The splendours of house and grounds, the atmosphere of gay frivolity, the elegant rituals in manners, speech and dress were entirely foreign to his own upbringing. Here he found wealth and culture expressed in material things—wonderful paintings by Gainsborough and Reynolds, elegant furniture by Chippendale and Hepplewhite, statuary in gold, silver and marble. The very buildings were wonderful in their symmetry and grace and the gardens and grounds were designed and laid out by masters of the landscape such as "Capability Brown".

Many were the stories that Dick told to his father about these great houses and their friendly owners and Richard liked to hear them because he wished to emulate his neighbours and show them that Richard Arkwright was a great man in a worthy setting. "I've no time to think of it now, Dick, but one day," he said, "I'll build a house as good as any of 'em and I'll fill it with furniture and pictures and such like as will be remembered long after I'm dead and gone!"

The new game of cricket was a democratic game in those days. Everyone who had ability was eligible to be chosen, from the rich man in his castle to the poor man at his gate and on the village greens and often in the parks of the great houses, factory hands, gamekeepers, gardeners and all joined in with their upper-class neighbours to play a match. Dick was a keen cricketer as were the three young Strutts, William, George and Joseph and he started a Cromford team with a pitch on the meadow by the Derwent. The spectators were just as varied in social status as the teams who played the game and on

73

one occasion Her Grace Georgiana, Duchess of Devonshire arrived in her coach.

She seemed fascinated by the sight and sound of the factories in the valley and asked a nearby spectator if the famous Mr. Arkwright could be brought to her carriage. Richard was very busy at the factory but such an invitation could not be ignored and, threading his way round the carriages and people in the meadow, he came face to face with one of the most beautiful and famous women in England. The great Arkwright whose word was law in so many factories, was almost dumb.

"I have so wanted to meet you," said the Duchess graciously. "We all like your son, but *you* are the one who has brought wealth and fame to our district, and we count it a great privilege to have you amongst us."

"It's an honour to meet your Grace," mumbled Richard, overcome with the charm of the great lady, and scarcely able to find his words.

"Come and sit with me a little in my carriage," went on the Duchess. "I'd like to know more of your wonderful machinery and the great cotton industry you have created."

The warmth of her manner, the genuine interest she displayed went to Richard's heart and he found himself chatting away with an ease he would not have believed possible.

"And I've been bidden to dine at Chatsworth!" he told Dick with great pride. "I never thought I'd come to that! I shall have to get over to Manchester and buy myself a new suit, for her Grace gave me so much notice, you'd have thought I dined out every day of the week! 'Can you spare me an afternoon, Mr. Arkwright?' she says to me, and it would have surprised her if she'd only known how I spend my evenings with a grammar book, learning to write a bit more easy like!"

"I told you how it was," laughed Dick. "She treats everyone as if he were the King himself and talks so gaily, you laugh all the time you're with her. You should hear her with her little dogs! 'Come along my teeny weeny woggie! Oo hasn't eaten oo's little din-dins' and such like!"

Richard was slightly taken aback.

"I must say she seemed friendly enough," he said. "And she'd got a friend with her called Lady Elizabeth Something-or-other, and they were two of the prettiest things I've ever seen in my life."

"That'd be Lady Elizabeth Foster," said Dick. "And to see her making sheep's eyes at the Duke would make you smile. They say she has two children tucked away somewhere and her husband won't give her a divorce, but it's hard to believe in the goings-on which they say take place."

"I don't hold with divorce, so don't mention the word to me again," said Richard stiffly, and he looked and felt unutterably shocked. If only Margaret would come to him and restore the pleasures and comforts of a home and family which he craved. And yet Margaret, he knew, would have no truck with gay Duchesses and the like and even the Duchess herself might well have hesitated before inviting him and his wife to dine at Chatsworth.

The day came when "he could spare an afternoon" to dine with Her Grace and he felt more relaxed as he alighted from his carriage and was conducted into the great house to meet her. She spent some time in showing him the treasures of Chatsworth and then they went out for a walk in the grounds where she pointed out the rhododendrons, azaleas and magnolias brought specially from China. Although he could scarcely tell a daisy from a buttercup he was entirely under the spell of the gracious lady beside him, and when she began to touch on the

75

subject of money and gave the slightest and most delicate but pointed hint, that she was in very temporary financial difficulties he felt only the delight and privilege of her confidence in him to keep her secret and help her out of her trouble.

"I loaned her a bit o' brass," he confided in Dick at the end of a recital of his adventure. "She's such a nice lady and so kind and thoughful—it were the least I could do, wasn't it?" The very thought of sharing a secret with the Duchess gave him great delight at the time although, when he became more knowledgeable about the recreations of this new way of life, he felt some sense of shame when he remembered this occasion.

"I should like Mother to see Cromford," said Dick one day. "And it's time that Susannah came to visit us."

His pretty sister often came to Rock House to see them both, and each time Richard loaded her with extravagant presents and even sent something back to Margaret with a polite message.

"Your stepmother can come any time she has a mind to," said Richard, but he shrugged his shoulders in an off-hand way as if her visit was of no great moment to him. "There's a party coming from Leigh to see the factory, and she's welcome to be amongst 'em, if she wants." Dick, anxious to arrange it, went over to Leigh, and Margaret agreed to a visit, but nothing was going to make her acknowledge that she had been wrong in the past.

It had been a proud moment for Richard when he had shown Margaret and the party from Leigh round his modern factory, and many of those who had laughed at Highs throwing his spinning jenny through the window, were now thunderstruck at what they saw.

Margaret said little and successfully hid her amazement, refusing to confess even to herself that she had been wrong in trying to thwart Richard in his early days.

Even Smalley had come back as a manager at Richard's invitation, for the latter was anxious to show that he had not forgotten the helper of his initial struggles, but he had parted from Kay in a fit of fury, when he discovered him in a petty theft of some tools. By doing so, he turned Kay into an implacable enemy, who lay in wait for several years and ultimately had his revenge.

It made Richard furious that Margaret would never refer to the wrong she had done him, but Margaret's unyielding nature would not allow it and Richard, to his own surprise, found himself actually hinting to her that they might forget the past.

"Have you ever thought on coming to live here?" he asked carelessly, but she firmly shook her head.

"You and I have been too long apart," she said proudly. "You and I must go our own ways, but there's no hard feelings." In fact she was intensely loyal to him when his name was mentioned and never said one word against him, but their lives were quite separate, and whilst Richard rose in the social world and mixed more and more with the élite of the county, Margaret lived her own quiet life, brought up Susannah strictly and well and never showed any longing for the man whose name was now a household word.

She heard on all sides how good Richard was as an employer, and how well he treated the hundreds of children who worked for him. Although they had immensely long hours and in parts of England their employment was a shame to the nation, with Richard, they knew every consideration and if they were found to be unfairly treated, it occasioned the instant dismissal of the "tackler" under whom they worked.

Margaret saw the difference between the white-faced boys and girls who earned their livings in Leigh, and the stronger, rosy-cheeked ones employed in Cromford and Matlock Bath.

Their homes in Cromford were better and cleaner, with scrubbed doorsteps and highly polished kitchen grates, where steel shone like silver; their food was of better quality and more plentiful, and the whole small town had an atmosphere of prosperity and cleanliness of which she highly approved, for the streets of most places were like open drains, dirty and unpaved save by a single narrow stepping stone.

Punctuality, regularity and high standards were demanded by Richard, but there were times when newcomers to the district who came searching for high pay, had to be treated with some degree of harshness. Women had been known to fight in the streets, but their behaviour was given short shrift and if it were found to occur again, they were summarily dismissed and their families with them.

Everybody from Richard downwards, worked unflaggingly.

All business at the factories started at six o'clock in the morning and a "knocker upper" would go from door to door, to wake the sleeping people. On cold dark mornings in the winter, the place was alive with the glow of swinging lanterns, as the workers hurried to the mills, summoned by loudly clanging bells; women and girls would wrap their shawls about their heads and shoulders, and walk swiftly, their clogs clattering on the cobbled streets, and at noon, mothers of families would run with basins tied up in white cloths, in order to give their husbands and children something hot for their dinners.

It was not uniformly drab throughout the year and one of the highlights was the public spectacle of "Candle Lighting", when a huge procession of workers, men, women and children, marched through Cromford, led by a foreman clad head to foot in white cotton, and a band and a horse-drawn lorry following, on which stood a boy working a weaver's frame. They paraded through the streets and the procession ended with a feast, accompanied by an unlimited supply of ale. Then there was music and dancing, flares were lighted, and the fun grew uproarious.

From the age of eleven onwards this was the great day of Susannah's year; she never failed to come to Cromford, and Margaret was prevailed upon by Dick to come with her. Richard would send his coach to fetch them, and they would drive at a terrifying rate over the unmade roads.

They stood as a family to watch the parade, but Margaret was hurried back to Rock House before the liquor began to take effect on the crowd and the rowdyism started.

"I'm right glad to see thee," said Richard to Margaret. "And it fair pleases me that thee's going to stay a day or two."

"I'm glad to come for a short time," answered Margaret rather distantly. "And I'll say you've a right to be proud, Richard, on what you've done, and I hope you'll spend all that money of yours in a wise manner. It's a grand thing to see all the workers enjoying themselves! I hope you give some of that brass to those who haven't got any."

"Aye and I do an' all," said Richard sipping his wine and thinking rather ashamedly of the Duchess of Devonshire, but it was a great era for benevolence and charity, and orphanages were springing up on all sides and for Richard's comfort, he had just presented £1,000 to the new infirmary in Derby.

Having known what real poverty was, he now enjoyed dispensing a little of his riches—but not too much. He guarded each penny carefully, but was ungrudging where his family was concerned, and frequently offered a little more financial help to Margaret.

He was unexpectedly hurt when she refused.

"Keep your brass," she said proudly. "I have all I need and it doesn't do Susannah any good to see it splashed about. We don't sit down to a banquet such as this in *my* house, and I wouldn't want for her to get accustomed to it."

"Well we've all lived simple," replied Richard. "But now that I can pay for it, I like to enjoy what I can afford, and good food and good wine have become a real pleasure to me. I still work harder than most, but it does me good of an evening to give way a bit, though I'm getting a bit porky like! Will thee not have another glass of wine?"

"One is quite enough for me," said Margaret primly, feeling a quite unaccountable glow creeping over her, and she had to confess to herself that the odd days she spent with Richard were far from distasteful. "Though I'd never live with him again," she vowed inwardly.

Her own existence was simple to a degree; she was a deeply religious woman and a staunch Non-conformist with an inborn scorn of anything frivolous and amusing. Though Christianity ordained that she should forgive Richard for any suffering he had caused her, she could not help feeling it was rather unfair that he had prospered so exceedingly well. She even began to see signs of revolt in Susannah, who was now old enough to be conscious of the difference between her father's and her mother's households, and only wished that her beloved Mamma could always be at Cromford when she visited there, but it was a situation which as a child she had learned to accept, and it did not trouble her acutely.

It only seemed strange that the father who was so kind

and generous, provided that she did not trespass on his time, had apparently done something of which her mother did not approve, but Susannah thrust it from her mind and decided not to trouble her head.

Richard adored her, but he did not miss family life as much as other men would have done, and it was Dick who drew his attention to the matter of Susannah's education.

"I do think that she should go to a proper school," said Dick solemnly. "She's going to find it difficult to mix with the people who are our friends unless she is taught more than Mother can teach her."

"Your stepmother did well enough without any proper schooling," said Richard a trifle grudgingly. "Not that I'm gainsaying you, but I'm not the one to know where she should go."

"It may be a bit selfish, but it would be nice to have her near here," went on Dick. "Mr. Strutt's daughters go to Mrs. Lattafier's Academy in Derby, and I think it's a proper place for young ladies. Would you have a look at it, and then we can talk to Mother?"

"Not much use sending me!" said Richard with a twinkle. "Mrs. Lattafier would soon find out what book-learning I've got! I don't much care what Susannah learns, as long as she can speak proper and know how to drop a curtsey in company, and as long as she's nearby and happy, I'm prepared to leave it to you."

Dick knew it was no good persuading further and he took it into his own young hands to interview the school-mistress and then to tackle Margaret on the suggested move.

Margaret was surprisingly amenable; she loved Susannah very dearly and felt it wrong to deny her the opportunities which her father's money made possible.

"If your sister wants it, I'm agreeable," she told Dick,

81

C.A.—F

and there was no question but that Susannah wanted it more than anything else in the world. Her anxiety to try this new venture pained her mother somewhat, but she had made up her mind that Susannah should never suffer in any way, because of the stand her mother had made, and fighting back the tears which were very near as she said goodbye to the little girl, she waved her off to the completely different life to which she was introduced by Dick.

It proved an enormous pleasure to Richard to have her in this fashionable environment; he bought her a pony, and at every opportunity she was allowed to visit Rock House and to ride with her father. Only Margaret, alone in Leigh, began to wonder where justification could be found, and if, after all, she had been wrong to maintain her unyielding stand against Richard.

Chapter Seven

Ada

Richard sat in his office at the Cromford mill and opposite to him were Strutt and Need with anxious faces, as they totted up columns of figures and made notes on what Richard was saying.

"It seems to me that we've already done enough," said Need. "What is the use of going on further when we've all got what we need in the way of cash in the last five years, and the water frame known throughout the world?"

"I'm not speaking of the brass," said Richard quickly. "But this Manchester Act is downright unfair, and if people would be a bit more forward-looking, it should have been done away with a long time ago."

"What's wrong with it?" demanded Need testily. "I can't see how getting the Act repealed is going to do us all that good."

"Dammit!" said Richard loudly. "Don't you realise that half the materials women wear are smuggled into this country? And I don't mean just any women, but as is well known, the Queen herself? If we could get permission to weave calico and dye it to any colour, there'd be such a fillip to the cotton and silk trades as hasn't been seen before."

"It's quite true there's a deal of smuggling," said Strutt quietly. "The Hindus can weave finer than we can and the silks from China are worn by all the people of fashion. It would do the country a power of good if we could stop some of it and make materials here of a better quality and what people would go out of their way to buy."

"We've done enough," grumbled Need. "Why can't you rest, Richard, without poking your nose into Acts of Parliament? It would only be another thing to worrit us and might do no good in the end."

"I think Richard has got summut," said Strutt once more. "And I'd be ready to go along with him in this, and I think you'd be wise to do the same, Samuel. You know we haven't found him wrong in his ideas up to now."

"Well, you're two to one," said Need gloomily. "I'm not grumbling about the past, but I say again, I think we've gone far enough, but you must do as you please."

He scraped his chair along the floor and walked out of the office without looking back.

"He can't see further than the end of that nose of his, the old b——," exclaimed Richard furiously. "If you don't want to go along with me, Jedediah, in trying to get this Act altered, I'll go alone, because I feel reet strong about it."

Strutt tapped the office table with his pencil and thought for a long moment.

Then he said slowly: "I think you're right, Richard, and I *will* go along with you, but you don't handle the old boy proper, and he wants a bit of coaxing when it comes to fresh ideas. You'd better leave me to deal with him, but you can count on me doing what I can, and I'd be ready to go up to London and see what I can arrange with the authorities."

Richard's face broke into a smile. "I hoped you'd see I was right," he said jovially. "It's a reet unjust law and if us can get it changed, it's going to do the textile trade more good than folks can imagine and be a smack

84

in the eye for the wool people too, what do all they can to stop our progress. Once we get the Act out of the way, there'd be no stopping us building mill after mill."

"You'd do better to keep your mouth shut about any more mills," Strutt said firmly. "We don't want to get on the wrong side of old Samuel, and he's not one for ought that's new. We'll get some letters written between the two of us and see how the land lies."

He left the room to return to his own office and Richard rang the bell impatiently for Dick.

"What a do!" he exclaimed mopping his brow. "There's Need saying 'We can't do this, or mustn't do that' when the opening is there for any to see! Sometimes I think I'll go crazed with trying to deal with him and with the other daft folk that can't and won't see what's good for trade, and for that matter, what's good for England. Tha must do some letter writing, lad, and I'll tell thee what to say."

He leaned back in his chair against the wall of the office which was warmed by the huge ground-level fire heating the factory.

"To me it's sticking out a mile what should be done, and nobody in the trade seems to know what good it's going to do them. Mark my words there'll be no end of bother from all the manufacturers and the wool people too, if I can get done what I want. Me and Jedediah, we're the ones what has got to do the fighting!"

Richard dictated a letter and Strutt wrote a letter, and the post chaise took them to the proper quarters in London, and eventually Strutt followed with a visit and proved to the authorities that over £13,000 had already been expended on the manufacture of calico, and if permission to weave and dye were given, it would be the means of a great expansion in the textile trade and a great increase in the number of people employed.

Whilst he was absent and the government decision hung in the balance, Richard was like a cat on hot bricks and went about with a face of thunder, quarrelling with all and sundry and finding fault with everybody.

Young William Strutt who was in the business on the same terms as Dick, felt convinced that the partnership was on the verge of breaking up, and that Richard in his fury with Need's unco-operativeness would possibly leave them all and walk out.

Even Dick was greatly disturbed at his father's cussed awkwardness and his violent temper when anyone questioned his actions; he was almost unbearable to live with and nothing was right even in his own home. He returned from the mill and grumbled at the cook, the food, the people who waited on him, and even at Dick, who would annoy him over some triviality.

He saw himself as an unacknowledged benefactor to mankind, harassed by the jealousy of men who were always trying to filch his patent rights, or to put some stumbling block in the way of his progress. It was only when Jedediah returned from London with his mission safely accomplished and the Act altered, that he began to calm down.

Richard and Strutt between them carried the day; the mills of Cromford, Nottingham, and Derby worked to capacity and the wealth of all three men continued to grow.

Yet in spite of the riches and with all the textile manufacturers flocking to Cromford for licences, Richard found it a hard fight against ignorance and prejudice and was deeply resentful of the jealousy against him and the fact that his fellow employers were unwilling to grant him the just rewards of his endless patience and hard work and that the altering of the Act was bringing prosperity to thousands.

"They don't like my success," he grumbled to Dick. "And I'd like to know where they'd be without me and Jedediah to fight for 'em. There's none would have had the guts to do what we've done, and now they're running round trying to make out that it was nought to do with us! Well, let 'em all come! There's none of 'em can teach me now and they know it!"

Sometimes even Dick with his great admiration of his father wondered if he were being a little ruthless and a little too boastful and ambitious.

He was like a tornado dashing headlong from mill to mill and bursting in on his managers when they least expected it; if anything was amiss, he would shout and storm and try to drive into his employees the dangers of slackness and incompetence.

"If tha canna mind the little things, tha canna mind the big!" he raged, and men anxiously watched out for his coming, for they knew that any second-rate service was useless to him.

Dick sometimes went to Leigh where Margaret lived in her humble home and would pour out his troubles to her, for there were moments when he found it difficult to get on with his father.

"He's a good man, though he's awkward," said Margaret loyally. "If you look back on the years, he's done nowt but good in the world, and his temper is only because he's so brimful of ideas, he can't stop himself, as I've good reason to know."

"I wish you'd come back and live with us," Dick went on. "I think you'd calm him down and he has nobody else, because Mr. Strutt's away in London where his wife has died, and Mr. Need can't do anything for him except rub him up the wrong way, and I often think it won't be long before they draw out of the partnership."

"More fools they if they do!" said Margaret stoutly.

"Though I'm not the one to talk when I've made my own life away from your father; but he's one of the greatest men in England, and I'm the first to say so, even if I don't want to live with him! Tell him I'll come for a few days in Susannah's holidays, because I'm lonely without her and I don't want to miss any time she's away from school."

"I only wish you'd make it more than a few days!" said Dick ardently. "He needs a woman to look after him and care for his house, for he's never in it from morn till night, and if Susannah and you were there, things might be quite different."

"I'll come for a week or two then," said Margaret rather unwillingly. "But as a matter of fact, Dick, I couldn't abide all the grand folk who seem to be your friends. I wouldn't fit in with them and you know it, so we're really best apart, but I'd do a deal to please you, so come I will some time or other."

With this, Dick had to be content and indeed he was so busy that he had little time to worry over his father. They now had mills at Belper and one at Bakewell, which was solely under his management and at which, from the moment he started, he made at least £20,000 a year.

With Dick gone from the house, the full weight of his loneliness came upon Richard and once again he found himself isolated from home and family. It was not Margaret he thought of—she had been taken as a partner rather than a wife and both had realised and accepted this. It is a fallacy to think that men and women of like natures make the best marriages—Margaret and Richard were too alike in nature for the give and take of married life. It was the memory of Patience—sweet, kind and affectionate Patience—that occupied his mind in these lonely days and he longed for a woman like her to share his life.

His meeting with Ada came about by chance and in an almost identical manner as that in which he met Margaret. He had gone to Bakewell to discuss some business with Dick and to call on a man in the town. When the door opened to his knock his heart missed a beat for there, standing by the man, was a young woman uncannily like Patience—"This is my wife Ada," said his host genially, "and we're both proud to welcome you, Mr. Arkwright, for you've certainly transformed our neighbourhood."

Richard murmured something unintelligible, for he was agitated by Ada's likeness to the great love of his life; she had the same soft prettiness, the same shy but charming manner and the same simplicity of bearing.

"Bakewell has done well to have an Arkwright mill in its midst," went on his host. "It's certainly changed the town a fair deal and brought employment where it's needed. We've all got a lot to thank you and your son for, and I must say, I couldn't have a better chap to deal with than Dick."

Ada had disappeared to see to the serving of the dinner and Richard having got over the shock of her resemblance to Patience, had settled down to a pleasant chat.

To dine at Chatsworth pleased his vanity without exposing his credulity but in the house of the Bakewell tradesman and his attractive young wife he felt really at home.

There was, indeed, a serving maid, but the plain wholesome dinner had been cooked by Ada herself and she flushed with pleasure at the great man's compliments which he made to her cooking. The adulation which he received here came from people of his own kind and had the ring of sincerity about it. It was just what his heart craved for—a fireside, a cosy chair and a quiet chat over a cup of tea with an attractive young woman ministering happily to him. When he praised the Derbyshire pudding she had made, she promised him the recipe, but the thought came to his mind that the giver was far more desirable than the gift and he felt disappointment when she excused herself as having much to do and left him with her husband. He learnt that she had no relations and no money of her own but, although his host admitted that he was "a bit on the old side" for her, he had given her a home and security and as far as he was concerned she was an excellent housekeeper, so that both of them gained by the union.

Richard could not dismiss Ada from his mind and when Dick, some weeks later, said that the Bakewell tradesman had died suddenly, he went at once to see her. She looked young and fragile in her widow's weeds and seemed overcome with shyness as with gentle dignity she asked him into the house. He expressed his deep sympathy at her loss and she had to admit, when questioned, that she was temporarily in financial difficulties but, when Richard offered to help her, she seemed almost to be offended—"Oh, thank you, sir, but I can manage quite well. It is only for a short time and things always sort themselves out, don't they? I'm young and strong and, if need be, I can work for my living. It isn't as if I had any family or relations dependent on me."

"Yes," said Richard gently, "I'm sure you can manage but—I'd be real glad to help in any way if ever you need it," and he hoped sincerely that she would turn to him for help some time. Ada thanked him for coming but, as she saw him out, did not invite him to come again.

Richard Arkwright could not accept that this was the end of their acquaintance and, visiting Dick at Bakewell a week later, he called at the house once more. He found that the maid had been dismissed and Ada had evidently been working through a mass of papers at her late husband's desk.

Richard realised at once that their conversation was conducted in a much more relaxed atmosphere and, while he carefully avoided any mention of money, he looked from the pile of documents on the desk to the rather harassed young face of Ada and begged gently that he might be allowed to look through them with her because he was more used to dealing with such matters than she. His obvious sincerity and kindness overcame her reticence and over a cup of tea and hot oatcakes he read each document and gave her the benefit of his great experience and helpful advice. She discussed her future plans with him as to a friend and told him that she was thinking of taking up a post as governess.

"I had a good education up to the time that my father and, shortly afterwards, my mother died," she said. "And I think I could undertake the upbringing of a young child, not of course anything beyond first lessons, but I can teach anyone to sew and make their own garments, and I hope I know good manners."

"You are very courageous," said Richard warmly. "If I can hear of somebody who would like your services, be very sure that I shall recommend you."

Ada gave him a strong, protective feeling and he would dearly like to have taken her under his wing and indeed into his household, but that would be something which would be hotly resented by Susannah.

He left with a promise that he would call again shortly, and this time Ada felt herself wishing that he would do so. It was not often that one was offered help from the famous Mr. Arkwright.

Ada's position in the world was a humble one; her friends were amongst the townspeople of Bakewell, none of whom she knew well, for she had not been married

very long having come from a home in Cheshire wit[h]
an old aunt who had since died.

The situation was perfect as far as Richard was con[-]
cerned. Ada was so like Patience in looks and manne[r,]
was such a lonely little person and lived a life so com[-]
pletely away from the people with whom he associate[d]
that his visits to her went unrecorded.

He took to riding over from Cromford, leaving hi[s]
horse in a livery stable so that there should be no tel[l]
tale carriage standing at Ada's door, and his visits gre[w]
steadily more frequent and friendly.

Finally he could hide his feelings no longer, told Ad[a]
what she had come to mean to him, and taking her int[o]
his arms, begged her to forget her worries and allow hi[m]
to become her protector.

In Patience's day, he had had a gentle charm wher[e]
she was concerned, and the same charm came to ligh[t]
again after years of lying dormant.

Ada capitulated, and from that day on had no mor[e]
troubles over money and knew a sense of real security
Richard felt a renewal of his youth, was like a boy i[n]
the excitement of his visits, rode over to Bakewell mor[e]
and more frequently, and took Ada with him in hi[s]
carriage on one of his excursions to Manchester.

"I cannot give you my name, my love," he whispere[d]
to her. "But in all else you'shall be as my wife, thoug[h]
the pleasure of having you at my home in Cromfor[d]
will never be ours."

"I wouldn't want it," said Ada humbly. "I'm not tha[t]
sort of body; I wouldn't like your grand friends, nor
they me, and I'm happier where I am—in the background of your life, giving you all the love you've not
had for a long while."

This arrangement and the attitude of Ada towards
their relationship was all that Richard could have hoped

or. He was well aware of the "affairs" in which his neighbours of the county indulged and that mistresses and illegitimate children were accepted in society on the one condition that "the affair" was kept quiet and conducted in a decent manner. Richard preferred, for the sake of his children, to lead his double life in secret and almost prided himself upon his careful management of his own liaison.

Ada had no social ambitions whatsoever, was content to remain anonymous, and blossomed into becoming a faithful, adoring wife in all but name.

It would have been unnatural if she had not produced children, and in due time two little girls arrived on the scene, to the great joy of their mother and deep satisfaction of their father.

If Dick ever guessed of his father's secret, he never mentioned it, but with a man of Richard's robust and virile temperament, it would have been remarkable if there had not been some outlet for his natural affections.

Finally, casting discretion to the winds, Richard bought a large house on the outskirts of Bakewell, and there Ada and her two daughters lived in comfort and affluence, but there was never a murmur in the outside world of what Richard was up to.

Satisfied and happy, Richard continued from strength to strength in his prolific businesses, and Ada was a pleasure to him in the background of his life and never presumed to push herself forward.

Chapter Eight

Opposition on all sides

His relationship with Ada completely altered Richard's personality. Where before he had lacked the softening influence of a deep personal affection, it now added warmth to his whole nature. It seemed in a curious way to increase his love for his own family, especially to Susannah, as if he were afraid that she might discover his secondary life and turn from him in disgust and disapprobation, when to Richard's mind there was nothing of which to be ashamed, and only the fulfilling of a side to his nature, which for years had been starved.

He now felt "complete"; assured of great affluence, he needed no wife or housekeeper to run his home and if there was waste in his kitchens, it hardly mattered, though the old habits of thrift died hard and his cook had to be prepared for the arrival of the master at any unexpected moment. He would enquire severely, "What became of the huge sirloin of beef which had only been served once?" and cooks who did not care for his interference, found themselves ousted quickly enough from their positions, but it only happened rarely, and after that cooks stayed forever, for they had high wages, a comfortable home and a generous employer.

He enjoyed good food, and as the years advanced, good wine, of which he became a great connoisseur. The whole neighbourhood was only too ready to accept invitations to dine with him and it was quite true that he began to put on weight.

"I don't have the time to take exercise and ride as I did," he said one day to Dick. "I think it would do me good to take a week or two off work, and go on one of those riding holidays that people talk so much about."

"That's a right good idea," said Dick and he added quickly, "Why don't you take Susannah for she'll soon be on holiday, and it would be a wonderful treat for her."

Richard's eyes brightened; he felt certain that the holiday with his daughter would meet with Ada's approval, for she was always anxious that his family life should never be disrupted.

"Yon *is* a good idea!" he said enthusiastically, and when Susannah arrived from school to spend a little time with her father, he stunned her by suggesting that he would take a rest from work, and that they should both embark on this fashionable adventure.

"I never have a spell off," said Richard. "And how would you like it if we went right into the country and spent some time away from the mills?"

"Oh Father!" gasped Susannah. "It would indeed be wonderful, and do you mean to take Dick too?"

"No, not Dick," said Richard firmly. "He must stay and see to everything whilst I'm gone, but if it'd please you, we could spend a night or two with Mr. Strutt's girls, and perhaps with Mr. Wedgwood near Stafford?"

Entranced at the idea, Susannah could hardly wait to set off, and accompanied by a couple of grooms, they rode over to the Strutts' home, when Jedediah was still away in London, owing to illness.

Elizabeth Strutt wrote to her father:

"Mr. Arkwright came here on Wednesday night, and brought his daughter, bearing a very pretty letter from her brother. And would you think it? a very elegant little watch which he bought for her in Manchester! On

Thursday morning they set off from here for Birmingham. My sister [aged 15] and Miss Arkwright [aged 13] in genteel riding dresses. They seemed very happy and talked of going to France, and they both swear to keep diaries of their adventures." Indeed they had a competition together to see who could keep the best journal.

The genteel riding dresses were cut-away green coats, frilled stocks, and tall beaver hats, and the cortège must have been a charming one, with two servants riding in the rear loaded with their baggage.

It was an undreamed-of experience for Richard to ride through the countryside accompanied by two pretty young things, one flourishing a watch which it had given him untold pleasure to buy, and listening to their happy chatter. He forgot his business affairs and had nothing to do but enjoy himself.

It was one of the sweet happenings of his life and he knew that Ada would never grudge the time he spent with his daughter.

They would ride until sunset and then sleep in some country inn, whilst one of the visits they paid was to Josiah Wedgwood, whom Richard had already met several times in Manchester. He was a good chemist and geologist and had recently been experimenting with different kinds of clay and their reactions in the furnace to a silica glaze in colour. Richard felt some sympathy with Wedgwood in his repeated trial and error, for had he not gone through the whole testing time with his own hair dye? He rejoiced that his friend had succeeded at last and began to turn out beautiful but inexpensive pottery for the ordinary people who with new comparative affluence could afford it, and choicer work of exquisite design, colour and craftsmanship for the rich.

The two men had much in common and each admired and respected the other. Both were inventors and

96

industrialists whose names and products were known throughout the world and although Arkwright, for his part, had little artistic taste he recognised in Josiah Wedgwood a man of his own kind and stature.

Thus, when Richard and his two pretty young companions arrived they found a warm welcome awaiting them. Susannah was rather overwhelmed by the grandeur of the house and was glad to have Patty Strutt as a companion to provide some cover for her shyness and Richard, seeing his daughter's admiration for Wedgwood's home, took an opportunity to whisper, "One day, love, we'll have a house as good and even better than you have yet seen" and Susannah's heart swelled with pride at the thought.

She was convinced that whatever her father prophesied was bound to come to pass for had he not gone against everyone's advice and ended by being a tremendously wealthy man? There was no doubt in her mind that the splendid house would materialise before long.

Meantime, visiting in beautiful country mansions was an experience that any young girl might envy, and her schooling at Mrs. Lattafier's stood her in good stead, for although she was young and shy, she could hold her own in good manners and her father radiated pride in her.

The breakfast parties to which many neighbours were bidden were the greatest enjoyment of the day. Conversation might be far above the heads of the two girls, but everyone was gay and fresh and the gentlemen could not indulge in the sleep-making habit of sitting so long over their wines as they did in the evenings, when Susannah and Patty begged to be excused and made their way, yawning, to the bedroom and the huge bed which they shared.

97

The riding holiday grew in excitement, for Richard was determined to visit France, where his machines were already spinning busily in the northern part of the country and their visit ended with a few days in Paris, which to the girls was a paradise of gaiety and luxury.

There were however rumblings of great discontent in the country, but the average person whom they met in Paris, seemed untroubled by the rumours. The city was gay and elegant, although the stench was worse than in London, and poverty much greater among the masses, but none of this was obvious to the two young visitors, who were only entranced by the elegance and fashion far outstripping anything seen in England.

Richard was entertained by many wealthy manufacturers, who might not have been of the "haut monde", but were generous to his party and impressed by the brilliant Englishman who had done so much for the textile industry; they made fun amongst themselves of his "fat, vulgar face", but they realised that he was a genius and only wished that France's industry could compete with that of England.

To return to her mother and her quiet, dull little home, was a trial to Susannah and to Margaret's distress she became increasingly discontented; it was all too obvious that she would soon want to spend more and more time with her father but Margaret, with the iron determination which was her great characteristic, made up her mind she was not going to give in, even if Richard begged her seriously to return to him. Always there was this battle between the two personalities.

At the end of his holiday, Richard returned as a giant refreshed, and went straight away to visit Ada, who gave him the same loving welcome he had come to expect, listening in flattering silence to the new plans he had in his mind.

Once more his boundless energy was seeking further outlets, and he was now intent on extending his cotton empire to Lancashire where the great mill at Birkacre was one of his first enterprises. The textile industry had now become the biggest in the country, and sometimes Richard was overwhelmed by his own achievements.

"I'm afraid we're in for a bad time," said Richard to Dick and his partners when he returned from a visit to Manchester. "There's a lot of trouble brewing underground and I don't like the look of things."

Strutt, Need, Dick and young William Strutt had been inclined to pooh-pooh his anxieties, but one Saturday evening at Rock House as they were sitting peacefully drinking their glasses of port, there was a sudden noise in the stable yard, and Richard's servant hurried to the dining room to say that somebody had ridden post-haste from Manchester and must see him at once.

"Show him in," said Richard, rising to his feet, then turning to those who were dining with him he said: "I've been afeared something was going to happen. Come, gentlemen, leave your ladies for a while longer and we'll see what's afoot."

The man who had ridden over was a foreman from Birkacre mill; he was mud-spattered and exhausted and his tale was a terrifying one. During the Saturday afternoon, hundreds of people had descended on the splendid new mill and had attacked it with every sort of weapon they could lay their hands on.

The managers and some of the work-people who were in the factory had been taken completely by surprise, but they had put up a furious opposition and in consequence two of the menacing mob had been shot dead, one drowned in the river, and eight of them wounded.

"There's more trouble to come!" he said to his

99

partners, "And maybe what has happened to some of their mates will put the fear of God into the rest of 'em."

He turned to the man who had ridden from Birkacre.

"Have summut to eat, and what's more important, summut to drink," he said. "And when we've all had a good night's rest, we'll get down to planning what we must do."

"It's all this expansion," muttered Need under his breath. "We should have left Lancashire alone. The people here don't have such designs."

Dick was all for travelling to Birkacre straight away, but Richard was too disturbed to spare him, saying that Birkacre was evidently in the hands of brave and loyal men, and it were best to see that the trouble did not spread nearer home and that all the Derbyshire mills should be prepared for evil days.

Need was frankly terrified, but Strutt was calmer. "We must set the defence of Cromford in train," he said. "When that is done—and surely no trouble will arise on a Sunday—then one of us must go to Birkacre."

Dick was the one who seemed to worry most, and alas! leaving Birkacre for one more day proved disastrous. On the Sunday, the mob, beside itself with anger, returned to the mill eight thousand strong, and burnt the factory to the ground. Josiah Wedgwood who was in the district at the time met them on the road; he had no fear for his own works near Stafford, but could see that the whole of Lancashire was in an uproar and that the fear of unemployment, not entirely without justification, added fuel to the fire. There was already distress caused by the war in America and the non-arrival of raw cotton; meetings were held on all sides and a policy of complete destruction decided upon.

Richard and his partners put both mills at Cromford

nto a state of siege, and though trade in Lancashire was at a standstill, Richard was convinced that the trouble would only be short-lived.

"It happens with any new enterprise," he said calmly. "They'll soon get over this mob outlawry, but meantime we've got to put a stop to any more damage."

The excitement was intense, and the Derbyshire mills were placed in readiness for attack, with the workers acting as defenders, and the three partners, plus Dick Arkwright and William Strutt, rushed hither and thither and were in a state of frenzied anxiety.

Cromford was well prepared to receive the irate mob, and the gentlemen of the district put themselves at Richard's service in defence of his work "which had been of such utility to the country".

"We're ready to arm the mills!" they said excitedly; rumours filled the countryside and though nothing untoward happened in Derbyshire, for the workers were behind Richard to a man, there was a far-from-distasteful wave of excitement.

Night and day the mills were on the alert, for Richard knew that Wigan, Bolton, Blackburn, Preston and Manchester were either visited or threatened by mobs bent on destruction.

All was quiet in Bakewell, and Ada calm, composed and utterly unafraid. "Who am I to anger a mob in any case?" she said laughingly, when Richard went over to visit her and make sure all was well, whenever he could slip away.

He also had fears for Margaret and Susannah in Leigh, for they bore a hated name, and sent for them to Cromford; they were bundled into his coach and driven with all possible haste to Derbyshire, which to Susannah was the best adventure she had ever known. They settled into Rock House and to her great disappointment and that of the martial young men of the district, nothing whatever happened.

It was an anxious time, especially as the trouble-makers had a certain amount of outside support from people who were blinded by the immense profits of the patentees and proprietors, of which Richard was the leading one.

The mills continued as usual, but on short time, as the supply of cotton from America had ceased and only imports from the Near East and the West Indies with whom Richard had always dealt, kept them going, but he continued to look after his work-people, who counted themselves amongst the very lucky ones.

Margaret resented having to stay a longer time than usual, and kept very much to herself. She would not appear when visitors were present, went for long solitary walks, and only unbent when the family was quite alone. Luckily for her there was little or no entertaining owing to the disturbed state of the North Country, and she was prevailed on to stay over Christmas.

The troubles died down as Richard had prophesied, and at the conclusion of the war with America, when people wept with joy as the first bales of cotton passed through the streets of Manchester, the workers found that trade was expanding, and suddenly there were no more riots.

It looked as if it were an act of defiance on Richard's part when in 1780 he built a large factory at Shude Hill in Manchester, right in the heart of enemy country. His ramifications had now become so great that Strutt and Need felt that he had grown beyond them, and they split up their partnership, dividing the ownership of the mills. Strutt had those at Belper and Nottingham, and Richard and Dick, now his father's partner, took over the rest. Need retired, for the final troubles had proved

oo much for him and the thought of arming his
factories with weapons of war, caused him to be
appallingly nervous. His partnership with Richard had
made him extremely rich, but had not been one of
unalloyed joy. He was thankful to sink into the background, to Richard's great relief, and not long after he
had ceased to take an active part in the business, he
died in London, thus removing for ever one very big
thorn in the flesh.

Some of the unease between the partners had been
Richard's insistence to try out a steam engine to work
the machinery and both of them saw their hard-won
fortunes being frittered away in further experiments.
With Jedediah Strutt, Richard parted perfectly amicably,
their friendship continuing unchanged, but as Richard
said to Dick : "Now we can go on with none to stop us."

When the steam engine was finally installed, there
was a fabulous increase in spun yarn; weaving mills
sprang up everywhere, although it took time, and it
was then that the golden age of the textile industry
really began.

When Richard had attempted to take out another
patent for a series of adaptations for carding and
spinning cotton, he was very disappointed when the
patent was refused him ; any attempt to thwart him
made him snarl like an angry lion, and he had retaliated
by bringing legal actions against people he swore were
infringing his patent rights. Out of nine actions he lost
eight, and Dick was the one who had to bear the full
brunt of his fury.

His troubles brought an increasing number of severe
asthma attacks and Dick and Susannah, who was by
then old enough to take her share in caring for her
father, had to wrestle with somebody who was most of
the time both arrogant and difficult.

The climax was reached when his enemies succeeded in bringing a trial at Westminster Hall against the man who had superseded them all, and Highs was able to give vent to his pent-up rage.

Richard rode over to Bakewell. "I'll not be seeing you for a while," he announced to Ada. "I've got to go to London for they're bringing an action against me for patenting the water-frame. Against me!" he exploded. "What has done for cotton what no man else has done!"

Ada calmed him down with assurances that he could not fail to win the law suit, but deep down nobody was quite sure that this was so; his greatest friends knew that there was an element of doubt. Kay joined with Highs in a blistering attack upon his old employer and the whole wretched story was raked over, even Kay's wife coming forward to say how she knew for certain that her husband had been persuaded to give away the secret of Highs' poor smashed-to-pieces jenny, and the judge in his summing-up agreed that there was little question that Richard had filched the ideas of other men, even though he was the man to bring the machine to its ultimate perfection, and that this final laurel must be stripped from his brow.

The trial began at eight o'clock in the morning and continued until 1 a.m. on the day following—a Sunday, by which time even the indomitable Richard was almost too tired to care about the result, but when the finding was made public, he was cut to the quick.

He thought of the years of his life which had been spent in unremitting labour, and he was still more hurt when a scurrilous pamphlet was printed saying that: "At last the old Fox has been trapped by his overgrown beard, but it is hoped that the dose administered would purge him from tyranny and unjustifiable claims, whereas he has made an immoderate sum of money."

The last sentence was the crux of the matter; his huge wealth was that which incurred the wrath of the North Country; they could not bear his prosperity, the position he had created for himself and his family, his notoriety and his world-wide fame.

Throughout the following uneasy months, apart from Dick and Susannah, it was Ada and her children who comforted him. Her house held no tension for him, and there he could relax and even sit back comfortably in his shirt sleeves, which he did not care to do in his own house; there he regained his boundless energy and zest, for nobody could hurt his position financially or otherwise, and when the unhappy few months were over, he sprang back into an active participation of life.

Chapter Nine

Willersley Castle

Dick had now taken a great burden from his father's shoulders, and Richard had time to think of other things beside cotton spinning.

He was in the forefront of those who saw the making of canals as one of the big steps in the transporting of goods throughout England and himself set about the constructing of one which connected Cromford and Derby.

"I don't know what Father will turn to next," said Susannah to her mother. "He never seems still for one moment, but it worries Dick and me that his attacks of asthma are so very severe."

Margaret's conscience pricked her when Susannah talked in this vein, and she often felt a pang of remorse that after the trial in the High Court had gone against him, she might have hurried over to stand by his side when he returned home.

"You'd best go and stay with him for a while," she said briskly to Susannah, determined not to show what were her inmost thoughts, and Susannah, who by this time had left school, packed her bags and began to make a more permanent home with her father.

She found him already aflame with the idea of building a house for himself, now that he was not so heavily involved in industry; he had always been deeply attached to Cromford Dale, and had bought a long stretch of the River Derwent, a wooded park and acres on all sides.

Willersley Castle

He and Susannah walked round the lovely stretch of country, and Richard showed her the site which had always been in his mind.

"I think yon would be a gradely spot," he said pointing with his stick to where a bluff of rock stood out from the hill side, completely hiding any sight of his mills.

"Let us go and look from the top," answered Susannah, and they climbed a steep slope and reached the limestone outcrop.

"What a view!" she exclaimed breathlessly. "But how could you build a house on the side of a hill?"

"Everything's possible if you've got the brass," said Richard simply. "I like the place and if you like it too, then that's settled, and here the house will stand".

He engaged the services of an architect from London and bade him spare no expense in constructing one of the finest mansions in the country. It took six years to build, but when finished, it was an impressive building, with gardens sweeping down to the River Derwent; the bluff of rock had been blasted away at a cost of £3000, before ever the work could start; then a steep, curving drive had to be cut from the hill side, where horses heaved enormous loads of building materials.

The house itself, built of local Derbyshire stone, was often condemned architecturally for its circular turrets and castellations, but it was a genuine example of Georgian romantic taste, the most interesting feature being a small circular gallery on two floors, with an echoing oval skylight, letting in the sunlight from the top.

Margaret came over from Leigh and thought it far too grandiose and ostentatious, but Richard was so wealthy that nothing seemed out of his reach. He boasted sometimes of his riches, saying that he could quite easily pay off the National Debt, and the building of Willersley Castle was as nothing.

He would pace up and down what was to become the terrace, looking down at the shining river and the beautiful trees which lined its banks. "I want it to be ready to enjoy and live in! Not to be finished when I'm dead and gone," he grumbled.

He planned to build and endow his own church in the park and fretted that everything could not be done at once.

"I've seen what you're doing in Cromford," Ada said one day when he visited her. "What a gradely house! You've given me a grand one, but nothing like you're building over yonder!"

Richard felt slightly uncomfortable.

"It will be Dick's one day if I don't live to see it finished," he said on a plaintive note. "And should I ever get there, I only wish I could take thee with me, but I can't and that's that."

"Don't you fret," said Ada comfortingly. "I've no wish for it, as I've always told you. I never go so far as a rule, but it just happened as I was took to Derby, and it was pointed out to me."

"And who took thee to Derby?" queried Richard jealously, for he had given much to Ada, but certainly no means of transport.

"If you want to know, it were the man who has the greengrocer's shop," said Ada almost snappily. "And he'd no idea I knew you, more than the man in the moon!"

"We mun be careful!" said Richard. "For now it's a bit awkward-like for me to come and see thee as often, for Susannah has chosen to live with me instead of her mother, and visits aren't so easy."

"Anyway I'm glad she's with thee, with your asthma and all," said Ada placidly, in such a contented tone that Richard felt a prick of jealousy over the greengrocer.

"I've got a new interest in some muslin mills at Stockport," he continued. "So when I go there, I can stop by with you and there won't be any questions asked. But I do wish I could be with you more often."

Ada sighed a little but did not seem particularly distressed and Richard felt the first qualms of uneasiness. But perhaps it was all for the best, for he had plans to be away much in the future, and when he was home, his attacks of asthma were not conducive to love-making. He was beginning to feel his years, and Ada was well provided for whatever happened.

His energies were already in another direction. He had become interested in the manufacture of muslin, and a new jenny had been constructed by Samuel Crompton which could spin finer than any materials from the East. Richard was also to help a man named Sam Oldknow to finance a new muslin factory. He had known Oldknow for a long time, and matters were brought to a head through an old friend called Salte, who was enthusiastic over the enterprise. "Whatever Arkwright touches will turn out well," he prophesied. "I hold his character in high esteem and greatly approve of this new venture," and from its inception, the weaving of fine muslin was highly successful.

Although his house was by no means finished, he was already setting in a store of furniture in readiness for its completion, and knowing little about such things, it was fortunate for his successors that men such as Chippendale and Hepplewhite were the craftsmen of the time, so that with every piece he bought, Richard could make no mistakes.

He purchased pictures too, and he and Josiah Wedgwood were the great patrons of Wright of Derby, who specialised in candle-lit pictures and moonlit landscapes of the Derbyshire countryside, although the chief source of his income came from his portrait connection.

Richard was painted by him several times, always dressed in a plain suit of buff-green cloth, with knee breeches, white stockings and shoes like clogs, and it was in this unostentatious dress that he was portrayed.

"I want thee to put in the rollers of the spinning frame," he ordered Wright. "It's them what made me the money I have, and I wouldn't want folk to think I'd forgotten where my bread and butter came from."

Other pictures were done in gayer colours, such as a plum coat with a yellow and black striped waistcoat, but in the last decade of his life, he had lost what looks he had as a young man, and was scarcely a romantic figure.

But he still had his indomitable energy and allowed himself to become involved in a scheme for Scotland with a man named David Dale and together they journeyed north, where a huge civic reception awaited the "Father of British Factories".

He was fêted in Glasgow, and made an honorary burgess of the City and a Freeman of Perth. It was a startling contrast to the treatment which had been meted out to him in Lancashire, which suddenly awoke to its hidden regard for him and was greatly disturbed by his sortie into Scotland. The gibe was that he would find a razor in Scotland to shave Manchester, and Richard threatened in a speech to put Lancashire out of business with his Scottish enterprises, but luckily it proved an empty statement, for the cotton industry having hated him bitterly, had now realised that it was to him they owed their prosperity.

Every time he left home, he would return praying that his new house would have made further advances towards completion, but it was a slow business and a frustrating one, and Rock House being so near, Richard could watch every detail of the snail-like progress. For one who habitually got everything done at top speed it was especially frustrating.

Then a particularly revengeful fate took a hand, for when Willersley Castle was ready for him to move in, a dreadful misfortune occurred and half the building caught fire, and although the elegant furniture was saved, part of the house was severely damaged.

Richard, Dick and Susannah stood watching the flames, and Richard, the hard-headed man of iron, had tears pouring down his cheeks, whilst every man in his employ at the mills, formed a human chain from the River Derwent up the steep slope to the house, with buckets of water passed from hand to hand.

"Perhaps I won't never live in it," gasped Richard choking for breath, for the smoke, not to mention his acute anxiety, had brought on a severe attack of asthma.

As the flames died down Susannah drove home with her father, calmed him and gave him hot inhalations, while the stench from the burning building followed them down into their very house.

Dick worked furiously carrying furniture to safety and stayed throughout the night as the fire faded to smouldering ashes, to assess exactly what was the extent of the damage.

"It's not as bad as we feared, Father," he said when he returned early in the morning. "It must have been a bit of woodwork near a flue in the kitchen which started the blaze, but I think it won't take all that long to put the place to rights, so that you can at least live in part of it."

This was something over which Richard had no control; it was no use to curse and swear and wring his hands with fury, as he paced up and down the terrace, breathing the fumes of smoke and water which came from the house; the sight of the devastation so distressed him that he even found no comfort in visiting Ada, and determined to go right away to Scotland, taking Susannah with him and doing his best to forget his frustration.

His friends in the district were as distressed as he was himself: letters from every side poured in and he felt that all he could do was to get out of sight and sound of the blackened ruin.

A visit away in lovely scenery and amongst people who liked and respected him, did its healing work and when he returned to Rock House, he took fresh heart and blossomed out into a fuller social life, entertaining on a lavish scale for both Susannah and Dick.

He loaded Susannah with jewellery, sent her to the most expensive dressmakers and provided her with beautiful horses to ride. He could no longer ride with her, but a young man named Charles Hurt, a landowner from nearby Wirksworth, seemed always at hand to act as her escort.

Richard became watchful, for the young man began paying regular and oftentimes unwelcome visits as far as Richard was concerned, to his beloved daughter.

She was a pretty girl and the fashions of the day were very becoming; she enjoyed wearing flowered brocades with a train, carrying embroidered muffs, and occasionally sporting a false rump.

She was very young and charming to act as her father's hostess and the presence of Charles Hurt began to be remarked.

"He comes here a lot," said Richard rather moodily one night. "I hope you know what you're doing, my girl, for I don't want my daughter to make a mistake such as I did."

Susannah flushed and flew at once to the defence of her mother.

"It has nought to do with me," she said fiercely. "And I don't know what brought it about, but it seems tragic that you're both so against each other! I've enough warning not to make the same mistake myself!" and to Richard's consternation, she burst into tears and rushed from the room.

"Now what's up?" he asked himself, and after a few moments he followed Susannah upstairs.

"I didn't mean to upset you, lovey," he said, using the word which had often been on Patience's and then on Ada's lips, and Susannah slowly walked towards him and put her arms round his neck.

"It's true, Father," she murmured. "I'm in a great taking over Charles, but he has said no word to me, and I don't know if he truly loves me or not. I wish— oh! I wish so much that he'd speak to you, or that you would speak to him!"

"If he wants to talk to me, I'll not harm him," said Richard.

"I think he knows that I need to look after you," said Susannah. "Sometimes you look at him rather sharply and as if you wished he weren't there!"

"I'm no ogre," said Richard gruffly. "But I won't have you trifled with."

"I'd never go far away from you," said Susannah. "But—but I do wish I knew if he loved me or not!"

She need not have worried herself, for Charles who was only twenty-one had been screwing up his courage for some time, and eventually appeared one afternoon, flushed of face, but firm in his speech, and requested Richard's permission to pay his addresses.

"I won't say no," said Richard non-committally, but his heart felt rather heavy, for Susannah had been the delight of his life since she came to live with him, and he thought of returning to his lonely existence was almost more than he could bear.

The trips over to Bakewell to visit Ada had come to be something of a trial now that he was getting older, and it flashed into his mind that he might bring Ada to Cromford, especially as Dick was little at home, but again his strong vein of snobbism made him realise he could do no such thing.

"Charles Hurt has asked if he can marry Susannah," he said unhappily to Dick, "And there's nought against it as I can see. He's got a big estate and I don't reckon he's after her brass, but she'll have to ask her mother before ought is settled."

"Funny you should speak of marriage," said Dick. "For I've been plucking up my courage to talk to you for some time now. I too want to get wed, and it's to one whom you know a bit about, as well—Mary Simpson who comes from Bonsall."

Mary was the daughter of one of Richard's mill managers, and a girl whom Richard had always liked.

"Seems as if everything happens at once," said Richard heavily. "But I can't see what's agin it, and tell her from me that she'll be right welcome."

Dick gave a sigh of relief for his father's approval meant a great deal to him. They had been through so many trials and tribulations together and there was a strong bond between them; as long as the girl he loved was made welcome by his father, it made the entire difference to his happiness.

At the same time, he felt distressed that both he and Susannah should be leaving the old man alone. Dick had heard whispers of the presence of Ada in the background, but he knew Richard well enough to realise that it would not be easy for him to bring her forward.

Once more he turned to thoughts of Margaret a
being capable of solving their problems, but he was no
hopeful of any more success in the future than there ha
been in the past.

Richard drove over to Leigh to see her and succeede
in bringing her back to Rock House.

"Susannah's your daughter as well as mine," he said
"And not without you approve, can she be allowed t
give young Hurt his answer."

Margaret, in all fairness, could say nothing; Charle
was good-looking, well-born and well off, but it mean
that Susannah was leaving her mother for good and all
and settling down in a district where her father was king

With as good a grace as she could muster, Margare
gave her blessing, and in a few months time, both Dicl
and Susannah were married, Susannah to live at Wirks
worth, though eventually when Willersley was finished
she moved still nearer, into Richard's old home at Rock
House, and Dick settled into a smaller house on the
outskirts of Cromford town.

Susannah's wedding reception took place at Rock
House and even after she was married, she was unremitting in her care of her father, whose asthma grew
worse with the years, but life was not the same for him,
and when the wedding festivities were over, it was with
something like real sadness that he watched Margaret
drive away in his carriage to her much more lonely home
in Leigh. Events helped Richard to adapt himself to a
life without even Dick, who for many long years had
been his constant companion.

To crown the year, Richard was chosen by the Wirksworth guardians as an appropriate person to present an
address of loyalty to George III on his escape from
assassination by a fanatic named Margaret Nicholson,
who had with one hand presented the King with a

etition and with the other, attempted to plunge a knife into his heart.

Luckily the knife did not even penetrate through the King's coat, Margaret was proved to be quite insane and lived out her life as one of the sights of Bedlam; but the nation had had a fright, and Richard having been chosen by the people of Derbyshire to present an address of loyalty and relief, he returned home a Knight of Villersley.

His friends and employees were delighted; his honour was felt to be personal to the cotton trade, and his friend Mr. Salte wrote:

"Mr. Arkwright was a happy mechanic; in his lifetime he received the reward of his ingenuity. It does not happen so in general."

To Margaret it was something that she could not possibly accept; to call herself "Lady Arkwright" was something she did not either want or deserve.

As long as she remained in Leigh she was plain "Mrs." to all the people she knew; she had refused to share with Richard his troubled time in Nottingham, and now she would not consider sharing his honour.

Chapter Ten

Homecoming

Richard had a temperament which was rarely depressed for long, and before he could settle down and feel really sorry for himself, a great honour was paid to him and he was asked to become High Sheriff of Derbyshire.

"I never thought this'd happen to me!" he exclaimed delightedly, and rushed off at once to see if he could persuade Margaret to share the honour with him and help him through his year of office.

Margaret was of course adamant; not only would she dislike it intensely, but she was much too diffident to embark on a period of being in the public eye.

"I'm proud of what you've done in spite of what I used to say," she answered Richard. "But all this is not in my line and you know it. Susannah no doubt will help you; she lives nearby and it won't take all that much of her time."

"I should have liked for it to be you," said Richard. "I've often wished we might let bygones be bygones."

It was the one and only time he came near to making an apology, and Margaret's rebuff was not nearly as caustic as usual.

"You'll do well enough without me," she said shortly. "People would only wonder where you'd raked up a funny old woman to sit beside you! Go on and enjoy it!"

Susannah was overjoyed; she and Dick had both inherited their father's love of entertaining, and the idea of acting as the High Sheriff's hostess was immensely attractive.

"As long as I don't have a baby yet to spoil the fun," she laughed eagerly.

Charles, who unselfishly agreed, admired his pretty wife in the new clothes her father bought for her, and Richard discarded his plain working cloth coat and breeches, and burst out into richly embroidered coats of silk with velvet breeches. After over fifty years of quiet and sober dress he now let himself go with a vengeance.

But before he took office, he visited Ada and confessed that he must forgo her comforting companionship; since he was to become such a well-known public figure in the county, it would behove him to be extremely careful and to have no shadow of scandal attached to his name.

He gave her a lavish sum of money, but she too realised that their happy relationship must be allowed to fade; she had always been realistic, and as Richard grew older, she let him see that his absences did not trouble her.

From first to last, it had been a happy, undemanding affair; she had her children and a comfortable position and more she did not ask, for she knew Richard's health was taking its toll, and she ceased to make any demands on him.

Richard drove rather sadly homewards, feeling that though he would undoubtedly see Ada, the romance had passed away, and he had little doubt but that she would marry again.

As Sheriff he performed his duties with great ostentation and still greater flamboyance. "His thirty javelin men were dressed in the richest liveries ever seen and during Assizes, he provided a plentiful table with the choicest wines."

His procession to the Courts was even more splendid than that of the King to his Coronation and he sat pompously among the legal fraternity in his black and silver suit, with his lace wristlets and ruffles, and spent money so lavishly that his year of office might never be forgotten.

It seemed as if he knew how to act the part, and the Derbyshire county was proud of him, considering him as a figure of romance, and talking often of the the remarkable story of his career.

He entertained everyone in the district with boundless hospitality, allowed himself to be flattered by the Duchess of Devonshire into yet further loans of money, but was also greatly loved by the less distinguished mayors of small towns and their ladies, with whom he slipped back into the broad north-country speech he had known as a boy.

It was an excitement for the country folk to watch him drive by at high speed in his coach, decked out in all his finery, and Cromford felt that they were getting their money's worth as he dashed past.

"God bless you, Sir Richard," they would call out, and it was the greatest reward that Richard could have.

It seemed to him that all he could now desire was the completion of Willersley, and at last the day came when the furniture was put back in place and he could move in.

The house was still not fully repaired, but the portion most damaged by fire was partitioned off, and he found he could exist in great comfort. Willersley had both dignity and charm, with its high-ceilinged rooms and delightful views, for though Richard could see the little town of Cromford in the distance, the mills were hidden, and he looked down onto the lazily flowing Derwent, which had passed through the rocky valley to run between meadows planted with beautiful trees.

In the gardens, Dick, who was a great gardener, had planted trees and shrubs, and the terraces outside the windows were ablaze with rock plants. There were splendid glass houses which Dick had filled with vines, and in later years, he was given a medal by the Horticultural Society for his new method of cultivating grapes.

Indoors, Willersley was magnificent, and it was indeed fortunate that Richard, having unlimited money but little knowledge or taste, should have lived at a time of great artistic beauty, when it was almost impossible to make a mistake in furnishing a new home.

He ordered a famous crested dinner service, the plates and dishes edged with purple and gold, and Josiah Wedgwood at the same time had made him an elegant present of two vases, which he proudly displayed, of which "Sir Richard Arkwright was particularly obliged".

There seemed little more that he could want, and the days of youth and his heart-breaking struggles, were like a far-away nightmare.

He was so delighted with his new home that he determined to celebrate taking up residence, with a splendid ball, to which all his neighbours came with enthusiasm, not unmixed with curiosity.

The colours worn by his guests were brilliant, the materials rich in quality, and the whole picture was one of great opulence and splendour.

The Duchess of Devonshire still relying hopefully on the generosity of her host to help her out of a lifelong scrape, was among the guests, together with all the notables of the county, who were genuinely devoted to Richard.

Both he and Dick wore gorgeous coats and waistcoats shining with gold lace, and their breeches were of silk stockinette. Wigs and perukes were still fashionable, and the ladies with their piled-up hair, often ornamented with real fruit or artificial feathered birds, and their dresses of great width over the hips, took up an immense amount of space.

It was to Richard an almost unreal pageant of beauty.

He may have been unpopular with his fellow industrialists, but he was loved by his own work-people, and the yearly "Candle Lighting" grew more enthusiastic as time passed, and finally in this first year of his residence, the procession, hundreds strong, made its way to Willersley, chanting a song to the tune of "The Roast Beef of Old England", in praise of Sir Richard.

Richard stood before them, a solid, undistinguished and much-respected figure, with the tears coursing down his cheeks and felt that it was the finest crown of his industrial life.

In spite of his wealth, his fame and the number of well-known men and women whom he could count as his friends, it was amongst his employees that his heart lay.

He regained something of the gregarious life he had led as a boy among men of his own generation and financial position who lived close at hand—men like Mr. Gell, whose name was perpetuated in the Cromford street of Via Gellia, Mr. Longsdon, a famous local sporting personality, and Mr. Salte, with whom he had had a business relationship of many years' standing.

It was a great joy to Richard to possess fine horses: as a lad in Preston he had grown up knowing how to ride on any old pony that was available and then in Bolton, when he had been given the job of going out and about in search of hair, he had owned a horse as part of his stock in trade.

Now that he was a wealthy country gentleman, he was famous for his four greys, which he handled with consummate skill as he drove swiftly along the rough tracks of Derbyshire, and in spite of being a hefty weight, he was still an excellent horseman. He took to hunting as a duck to water, and though he was at least forty years old before he had the money or the leisure to indulge in it, when the time came he was an enthusiastic follower of the High Peak Harriers. He vastly enjoyed the excercise, loved a strong keen horse and felt nothing but excitement and exhilaration at jumping some of the fearsome grey stone walls which surround the fields in the Harrier country.

When the meet was at Mr. Longsdon's house at Little Longstone, where he had been bidden to bring as many friends as he could, there was always a glass of hot toddy, or port and madeira handed round to all those assembled outside in the cold morning air. Richard liked the convivial gathering, the chatting and the jokes, and strolled about glass in hand, talking to everyone before they moved off in the direction of Monsal Head, and one of the finest views in Derbyshire. There were rolling hills and rocks and woods and water, for deep down in the valley ran the River Wye, flowing from Millers Dale, broad and gentle as it wound through the bright green meadows, the very place in all the world to hunt a hare or a fox.

Tingling with excitement, the field moved away, with Richard, to whom lovely scenery meant a great deal, more appreciative than most others of its beauty.

There was Putwell Hill and the whole of Monsal Dale below them, and it was part of the pleasure of hunting to ride hard all day, knowing they were to return to the Longsdons' manor house and a rollicking dinner. Ladies were rarely present. A man could round off the day with more talk and more bawdy jokes, and endless glasses of good red wine with port to follow.

"By God! I enjoy it!" Richard exclaimed. "I've not had much time for fun in my life, and this makes up for everything!" But always when he entertained at Willersley and the old boys went cheerfully home, helped into their carriages by their coachmen who had been lavishly entertained in the servants' hall, Richard would walk slowly up to bed, carrying a flickering candle and feeling that his home was very big and very echoing in its silence.

His business activities were gradually slowing down, though he always had a finger in every pie and gave his opinion on every question raised, whether asked for or not, but apart from his interest in the muslin mills at Stockport, he had made enough money in his lifetime, and was not interested in making more.

The only thing that roused him to his old fighting spirit was his irritation with the Duchess, who never ceased to worry him for money, and Richard realised what a grave mistake he had made through his snobbism in helping her with her gambling debts.

Finally he drafted a letter to her which was executed by Dick, for Richard rarely wrote one himself, and only signed his name. In it, he now insisted on repayment and he gave the dates on which the money had been due and had never arrived.

He insisted too that he had always kept their business dealings entirely secret, and in a cloak and dagger atmosphere, asked her to reply to him at the Inn at Cromford.

The days had passed when Richard had to try and ingratiate himself with his distinguished neighbours, and the letter even contained suggestions of talking matters over with the Duke himself.

Although he ended his note: "With great respect, Your faithful servant", it is extremely doubtful whether Richard felt either respect or faithfulness, and he was now in a position that he could snap his fingers with impunity at any member of the aristocracy.

The Duchess, did not repay him herself, but the interest on the loan did not afterwards fail to arrive, for at last she had to confess her debts to her husband, and also that she was pregnant by Lord Grey. The Duke swiftly despatched her abroad.

It was the finish of the lovely Duchess, and never again did Richard lend money without security.

To the end of his days, Richard was proud and boastful of the wealth he had accumulated, starting from the time when he saved candle ends and bits of soap and put by every available ha'penny in his tin box.

He talked largely of buying up the cotton of the world, but quite suddenly ill health barred the way.

His sickness was chiefly the result of being alone in his great mansion; Susannah frequently visited him but it was not the same as having her always beside him, and now Dick was married he had little time to see his father except when Richard walked gallantly down to his office, which he did on most days.

Dick had not let the grass grow under his feet, and every year as regularly as clockwork, a new member of the family was produced, for evidently the blood of his grandfather Thomas Arkwright of Preston, coursed in his veins, and Richard was proud of his constantly recurring grand-children.

He enjoyed the thought that his name would go on through the years to come; Dick had been a source of comfort and support to him throughout his life and it gave him untold joy to think of the wealth which he would be able to pass onto his son. Little did he realise years later at Christmas, Dick was to stun his children with his generosity as they sat at breakfast, unfolded their napkins and each found a Bank of England note for £10,000 hidden inside.

His own family had taken little part in his life, though

his spinster sister Dorothy, sometimes came to visit him at Cromford; the remainder of his brothers and sisters had faded into the background, for communications were not easy and Richard was a poor hand at correspondence. Besides Dorothy, his brother Thomas was the only member of the family of whom he had any news, and Thomas, who now lived in Kendal, had won a prize of twenty-five guineas for an endless-chain device used in bringing minerals to the surface of a mine, and had obviously something of the same inventive turn of mind as his younger brother.

Of the numerous nephews and nieces who featured in the will which Richard had drawn up when his financial position was assured, he had no personal knowledge whatsoever.

He felt a glow of happiness at what he was able to do, but this did not prevent him having his moments of great loneliness, and he positively loathed the evenings which he had to spend by himself.

"I am worried about Father," Susannah told her mother. "He is not himself at all and is beginning to take little interest in outside events and only minds about Willersley, which he loves so dearly, but I am afraid he is very lonely, and Dick and I are not able to spend time with him as we used to do."

"What about those grand friends of his?" asked Margaret briskly.

"Well you know what friends are!" exclaimed Susannah. "They do visit him, but he is nearly always alone in the evenings and doesn't care for the parties he always enjoyed."

"And why are you are talking to me like this?" enquired Margaret.

"It's only because I'm always hoping that one day you might feel you could go to him," said Susannah frankly. "He's been such a good father to Dick and to me, so generous and kindly. And he's done so much for the whole country, and now the country can't do anything for him."

"If he's lonely . . ." said Margaret slowly. "But I never could abide the smart folk who came to the house, and all those parties!"

"Mother, if you could just see your way to visiting him for a short time," went on Susannah. "I believe he'd like it more than anything."

"I don't like to think he's alone, especially if he's not up to much," said Margaret, in the knowledge of her superb health. "Tell him I'll go for a short while and see what he says."

Susannah hesitated. "I think if he knew you were coming out of pity, it would rile him terribly. Now he's ailing, could you not say that you too were lonely and would like to be with him?"

Margaret flushed. "He left me once," she said. "Not but what he hasn't asked me to return! But my pride takes a bit of swallowing.

"You're such a good Christian," went on Susannah. "I didn't somehow think that pride would enter into it. I thought perhaps," she went on softly, "You might like to think you had given him a little happiness before he died."

The flush on Margaret's cheeks faded and left her rather pale.

"You didn't say ought about dying!" she exclaimed.

"I didn't say, because he isn't," snapped Susannah. "But his attacks are sometimes frightening, and he does act if he were dead tired, so Dick and I are worried."

"Well, I'll go to him, but we'll see for how long. And I don't want his carriage sent for me, or anything like that; I'll make my own way."

"That's senseless!" exclaimed Susannah. "When Dick is in Manchester every week : he has only to send his man over to fetch you, and Father need know ought about it until you step into Willersley."

"That house!" sighed Margaret. "And all those servants!"

But she agreed to go and Dick's carriage fetched her and drove her to Cromford.

It was a lovely night in early spring; primroses and daffodils carpeted the sloping lawns to the river, and Richard sat for almost an hour on the terrace in the late sunshine. Then he shivered a little and walked in to sit by the fire in one of Willersley's large rooms.

He had spent the morning in his office; Dick seemed to have the many business affairs well in hand, and Richard listened for a long time to his schemes for improving the mills, making better heating and ventilation arrangements and even going so far as to suggest that the children they employed might remain in the free school which Richard had given to the town, for a whole year longer.

"It don't do them no harm to work," Richard said testily. "I began younger than what they do nowadays, but I don't care what you arrange as long as the output don't suffer. They'll be making you a member of the Royal Society if you put forward these new-fangled ideas, which is what they should have done to me, if it hadn't been for those bastards who were my enemies!"

He had walked home up the steep drive, after his chat with Dick, and found himself as he often did nowadays, rather breathless.

Nobody had come to see him and he had drunk his glass of madeira alone, and now he slipped off his coat, loosened his stock, and sat waiting for his four o'clock dinner to be announced. He always ate early when there was no one to keep him company, and retired in good time to bed. The sun had gone now, but there was a glow in the sky and it was not yet dark. The butler came in to draw the curtains and Richard stopped him.

"Don't waste the daylight," he said peremptorily. "You can draw them in half an hour when you bring in the candles."

As he spoke there was a clang from the bells hanging in the passage. "I should think a visitor, Sir Richard," said the butler, hurrying to the door, and Richard began to scramble into his coat.

"Lady Arkwright!" said the butler in loud tones, and Richard turned quickly, his face lightening into a delighted smile.

"My dear Margaret!" he cried. "To what do I owe this pleasant surprise?"

Margaret came forward very slowly.

"Times change," she said in the brisk voice she always used. "We're getting no younger, Richard, and lately I've begun to feel a bit more lonely than I used, and I had a mind to come and see thee."

"I won't say that I haven't wished for this," said Richard, putting his hand on her shoulder. "You know I've told you you're always right welcome! Shall I ring for your trunk to go upstairs?"

"I've already told that grand chap what came to the door," said Margaret briefly. She stretched out her hands to the warmth of the fire. "I've thought of coming over for some while back, and then I began to wonder if I wouldn't ask Dick to fetch me when he was in Manchester, and drive over with him."

"But Dick weren't in Manchester!" said Richard quickly.

"He sent his man," said Margaret. "I'd a mind to

come by myself. It's a long time since we had a chat over the old days."

A broad smile came over Richard's face.

"Sit down! Sit down!" he said cheerfully, drawing up a chair for her. "I'm right glad to see you, my dear, and how long may I expect to have the pleasure of your company?"

Margaret had seen in the fading light that Richard looked much older and his breathing was not so easy.

"I'd planned to stay a while if I weren't in the road," she answered.

Richard again patted her shoulder, coughed with emotion, then sat down quickly in a chair at the opposite side of the hearth.

"I hope you'll not be going away again," he said briefly. "I'll ring to say we'll be two for dinner, though I expect they know it in the kitchen. And now what's the news of old Leigh?"

He made no further ado about Margaret's arrival and indeed it was never mentioned again; they just accepted each other, and the days slipped by in an extremely quiet and matter-of-fact way. It was unlike either of them to say much.

Margaret never again mentioned that she might return to Leigh, and Dick and Susannah both knew better than to question her; she was just there, and nobody discussed her arrival.

Grandchildren came and went, Richard made sorties to his office and sometimes they drove to Stockport, although now Richard did not take the reins himself, but mostly they sat in the garden and had long talks and still longer companionable silences.

Richard seemed remarkably happy; his energy had failed and he was content to remain at home, where he was no longer lonely, but during the warm summer months, his health began to deteriorate, and when August came, he just slipped away.

On the day he died, in 1792, a small flag floated at half-mast over the castle, and there was a stunned distress at the passing of a beloved figure in the county.

They hung the outside of the house with black, and when his funeral procession left for Matlock, hundreds lined the hilly road and climbed amongst the rocks and trees to watch the slowly winding cortège as it went on its way, preceded by a band of pipers who had come from Scotland to pay their last respects.

The "happy mechanic" had gone home.